ISBN: 978 1 873609 42 2

Design Daniel M. Eskenazi, London
Typesetting Daniel M. Eskenazi and Clare Milligan
Photography Daniel M. Eskenazi, London
Printed and originated by Graphicom Srl., Vicenza

# ESKENAZI

Six Dynasties art from the
Norman A. Kurland collection

*Part one*

2 - 25 November 2017

ASIAN ART
IN LONDON

**10 Clifford Street**
**London W1S 2LJ**
Telephone: 020 7493 5464
Fax: 020 7499 3136
e-mail: gallery@eskenazi.co.uk
web: www.eskenazi.co.uk

Norman A. Kurland, London, 2017.
Photograph by Daniel M. Eskenazi.

## Foreword

I first met Norman Kurland at the Carlyle Hotel in New York at 11am on the 1st of December 1986. We were introduced to one another by a mutual friend, Nicholas Grindley, the well-known dealer in Chinese furniture, who was keen for me to meet a collector from the West Coast of America interested in acquiring Chinese earthenware figures. It turned out that Mr Kurland was to be the first man I had ever met who, as far as collecting aims were concerned, exclusively targeted the acquisition of the grey pottery figures that furnished tombs in China in the Six Dynasties period (220 - 581). Neither the products of the previous dynasty, the Eastern Han (25 - 220), nor those of the Sui (581 - 618) that came right after, were in his sights, inasmuch as it could be determined what might have been made in 580 and what in 582. The Tang (618 - 907), rich in material culture and dear to so many highly discerning collectors was, bafflingly, considered an entirely unnecessary distraction.

Needless to say, I was much intrigued by Norman's choice within the strict parameters he had set himself. I, too, had a great liking for Six Dynasties tomb figures, having been schooled in my appreciation as a young man by the New York collector Ezekiel Schloss, who owned several excellent examples. As with Schloss, it was the sculptural variety of these pottery figures and the detail that was so evident in the modelling of them (because unglazed, unlike so many Tang examples) that fascinated Norman. On the reasonable assumption that Chinese burial practice mirrored the life that was lived by the human inhabitants of the tombs interred with its furnishings, they seemed to open a window into an unexpected world of varied and lively multicultural interaction.

Norman had already bought a few pieces by the time we met and his first purchase from us was in April 1987. He would go on to acquire some further sixty-five pieces in the following decades. Although I find much to enjoy and appreciate in Six Dynasties earthenware figures and ceramics in general, I must admit that my greatest love, of all the cultural artefacts of the period, is for its Buddhist sculpture, so magnificently represented in the carved cave temples of Yungang, Longmen, Gongxian and Xiangtangshan, as well as in the freestanding stone images of the sixth century and the smaller and exquisite gilt bronzes of the Wei period. Norman had not yet investigated this aspect of the culture of the period and took some persuasion to commit to this particular path. I spent many happy hours explaining my view that perhaps the most important artistic achievements of the period that held such fascination for him were expressed through its engagement with Buddhism. As soon he became convinced of this, no-one could have been more enthusiastic and his collection now holds prime examples of Buddhist art as well of the ceramics that so attracted him at the beginning. As the years went by, a very strong friendship developed between us and we spent much time together discussing the particular qualities that distinguish the art of the period, as well as its influence on the Chinese art that was to follow.

As a collector, Norman never made a snap decision when contemplating a purchase (unless in the privacy of his own mind and not shared with me). However, he consulted his wife, Deborah David, an accredited mediator and faculty member of CEDR (Centre for Effective Dispute Resolution), on every occasion and they always spent some time discussing the merits or otherwise of a possible future acquisition. It was Norman himself, though, who let us know if it would be good or bad news as far as we were concerned.

A love of early Chinese art inspired Norman, a graduate of both Princeton and Harvard Universities, to enrol as a student on two Masters of Art programmes at the School of Oriental and African Studies, University of London. In 2008 he graduated in History of Art and Architecture (Chinese Art and Architecture) and in 2012 in Islamic Art and Architecture. As if this were not enough, in 2015 he

completed a hat-trick of artistic M.A.s, at The Courtauld Institute of Art, London, investigating 'Buddhist Art: History and Conservation'.

Norman is a great wit and notable raconteur, qualities no doubt honed during his Hollywood years. Over the course of our friendship, we have shared many jokes, stories and situations. One evening, in a packed party at the gallery for the opening of an exhibition, two visitors were inspecting a display cabinet and turned to Norman who was standing nearby. 'Who on earth would buy such an ugly thing?' said one. 'Look! It's been sold – it has a red sticker.' 'There's no accounting for the taste of rich people,' said Norman 'but I'm delighted to say it was me.'

I would like to thank another mutual friend, Annette Juliano, for the truly informative and thoughtful introduction she has written to the catalogue that so cleverly and appropriately uses examples from the Kurland collection to illustrate her wider historical narrative. Over the course of decades, she has illuminated the Six Dynasties period with her scholarship, for which everyone is greatly in her debt. I still clearly remember the groundbreaking exhibition she organized at the old China House Gallery in New York in 1975 and have been an eager reader of all her subsequent articles and catalogues. Sarah Wong has researched the objects in depth and, with Philip Constantinidi, has written the catalogue entries. Yuansheng Wang has spent many days combing through the books in our library, both in English and Chinese and has translated all the descriptions in the catalogue into Chinese. Mr Lin Yi-hsin has provided us with an admirable translation of Annette Juliano's introduction. Jemma Kirkcaldy and Dominika Mazurek have greatly assisted in administration, the former by checking all our archive material in relation to Norman's acquisitions, the latter by dealing with a mass of current correspondence. Daniel Eskenazi has taken beautiful photographs of the objects in the collection that admirably illustrate why this is such an important and fascinating epoch of Chinese art and has been responsible for the design and typesetting of the catalogue. Finally, my heartfelt thanks go to Norman and Deborah who have entrusted us with the sale of their collection of which the current selection is only a part. We look forward to presenting part two at the same time next year, in 2018.

Giuseppe Eskenazi

*Left* catalogue number 27
**Limestone Bodhisattva** (detail)
Eastern Wei period, 534 - 549
Height: 68.0cm

1986年12月1日上午11点，我首次在纽约凯雷旅馆会见 Norman Kurland。透过一个共同朋友 Nicholas Grindley 的介绍，我们得以认识彼此。他是一位知名中国家俱古董商，很热衷于我与这位来自美国西岸并对购藏中国陶俑有所兴趣的藏家碰面。结果发现，就收藏旨趣而言，Kurland 先生是我见过专门针对中国六朝 (220 - 581) 墓葬灰陶人俑购藏的第一人。在他眼中所关注的，不是前朝东汉 (25 - 220) 遗迹，亦非后代杨隋 (581 - 618) 文物，而是尽量确定哪些作品是制作于580年而哪些又是完成在 582 年。至于拥有丰富物质文化且受到高度眼界藏家欢心的唐代 (618 - 907) 品项，则令人费解地对他来说，却被认为是全然无需的分心事物。

当然，对于 Norman 以其自设严格准则的挑选决择，让我感到十分好奇。其实我自己也很欣赏六朝墓葬人俑，在年轻时曾受教于纽约藏家 Ezekiel Schloss 以培养鉴赏能力，当时他曾拥有几件佳作名品。与 Schloss 一样，这些陶俑的雕像多变与塑模的明显细节（因为没加釉料，不像许多唐代作品），无不让 Norman 感到着迷。在合理推断下，中国丧葬实践反映生活情况，也就是墓主人物与其日用陈设的埋葬共存，它们似乎打开一扇窗口，进入一个意想不到变化生动的多元文化互动世界。

当我们相遇之前，Norman 已买入几件器物，后来至 1987年4月，他首次于我们店里消费。在接下来的几十年里，他陆续购藏65件作品之多。尽管一般我对六朝陶俑和瓷器相当喜欢与欣赏，但我还是必须承认，在那时代的所有文物当中，我的最爱仍是佛教雕塑，如同云冈、龙门、巩县和响堂山之开凿石窟寺里的宏伟表现，以及六世纪的单件石制造像与北魏时期的小型精致鎏金铜像。当时 Norman 还尚未对六朝文化加以探究，但仍接受而致力于这条特殊的收藏之道。我曾花了许多时光来解释我的观点，说明也许六朝时代最重要的艺术成就，即为透过与佛教的接触而表现出来，这也是让他为之着迷的地方。一旦他信服了这点，没有人能像他如此般投注热情，以致现在他的收藏中有着佛教艺术的精品杰作和最初吸引他的陶瓷器物。随着岁月更迭，我们之间发展出非常深厚的友谊，并曾花费许多时间一起讨论凸显六朝艺术的特质和其对往后中国艺术的影响。

当考虑购藏时，Norman 从来不会做出随意决定（除非他藏于内心而不与我分享）。不过，他会向妻子 Deborah David 进行谘询。她是一位认证的调解专家，为 CEDR（有效争议解决中心）的职员。在每一次场合中，他们总是会花点时间讨论优点益处或是其他未来购藏的可能性。但就我们所知，还是 Norman 他自己来告知我们结果消息的好坏如何。

作为普林斯顿和哈佛双料毕业生的 Norman ，出于对早期中国艺术的喜爱，启发他再次求学于伦敦大学亚非学院的两个艺术硕班学程，成为一名学生。2008 年他从艺术与建筑史（中国艺术和建筑）专业里毕业，之后亦在 2012 年修业完毕伊斯兰艺术和建筑学科。但这彷佛还不够，2015 年时他更连三抢元，获得伦敦科陶德艺术学院的艺术硕班学位，专研「佛教艺术：历史与修复」项目。

Norman 是一位优秀的机智才子和出众的健谈对象，这些特质无疑是他于好莱坞时所磨练出来的。在我们的友谊交往过程中，我们曾分享许多趣闻、故事和情景。某天傍晚，在艺廊展览开幕的热闹聚会里，有两位观众正在审视展示橱柜，其中一名转向站在旁边的 Norman 说道：「到底谁会买下这么一个丑陋东西？你看看，它已经被出售了－它有个红色贴纸。」此时 Norman 回答：「富人的爱憎好恶是无法解释的，但我很荣幸地要说那个人就是我。」

　　我还要感谢另一位共同友人，Annette Juliano，她为图录撰写相当详实且深思熟虑的导论介绍，并极为聪慧和适当使用 Kurland 藏品为范例说明，来描绘她广泛的历史叙述。几十年来，她以其学术成就阐明六朝时代，让每个人都获益良多。我至今仍清楚记得，她在 1975 年于纽约昔日中国之家艺廊所筹办的开创性展览，更成为所有她日后文章和图录的热切读者。王嘉慧对文物作品的深度研究，并与 Philip Constantinidi 撰写图录条目。汪垣生在我们的图书馆中梳理查找各类中英书籍，并把图录说明译成中文。林逸欣为我们提供 Annette Juliano 导论的出色译文。Jemma Kirkcaldy 和 Dominika Mazurek 在作业行政上极力协助，前者检阅所有我们档案材料里与 Norman 购藏的相关资料，而后者则处理大量的近日往来通讯。 Daniel Eskenazi 对藏品物件所拍摄的优美照片，绝妙地展现出为何这是中国艺术如此重要且迷人的时代，此外他也负责图录设计和排版工作。最后，我要由衷地感谢 Norman 和 Deborah，能委托我们来对其藏品进行展销。而当前入选作品只是一部份而已，我们期待来年在 2018 年的同时期得以展示第二部份。

Giuseppe Eskenazi

# Chronology
## Chinese Dynasties and Periods
中国朝代

| | | BC 公元前 | | AD 公元 |
|---|---|---|---|---|
| **Xia period** | 夏 | 2100c – 1600c | | |
| Period of Erlitou culture | 二里头文化 | 1900 – 1600 | | |
| **Shang period** | 商 | 1600c – 1027 | | |
| Zhengzhou phase | 郑州阶段 | 1600 – 1400 | | |
| Anyang phase | 安阳阶段 | 1300 – 1027 | | |
| **Zhou period** | 周 | 1027 – 256 | | |
| Western Zhou | 西周 | 1027 – 771 | | |
| Eastern Zhou | 东周 | 770 – 256 | | |
|   Spring and Autumn period | 春秋 | 770 – 476 | | |
|   Warring States period | 战国 | 475 – 221 | | |
| **Qin dynasty** | 秦 | 221 – 206 | | |
| **Han dynasty** | 汉 | 206 – | | 220 |
| Western Han | 西汉 | 206 – | | 9 |
| Xin dynasty (Wang Mang) | 新（王莽） | | 9 – | 23 |
| Eastern Han | 东汉 | | 25 – | 220 |
| **Six Dynasties period** | 六朝 | | 220 – | 581 |
|   Three Kingdoms | 三国 | | 220 – | 280 |
|   Western Jin | 西晋 | | 265 – | 317 |
|   Eastern Jin | 东晋 | | 317 – | 420 |
|   Liu Song | 刘宋 | | 420 – | 479 |
|   Southern Qi | 南齐 | | 479 – | 502 |
|   Liang | 梁 | | 502 – | 557 |
|   Chen | 陈 | | 557 – | 589 |
|   Sixteen Kingdoms | 十六国 | | 304 – | 439 |
|   Northern Wei | 北魏 | | 386 – | 535 |
|   Western Wei | 西魏 | | 535 – | 557 |
|   Eastern Wei | 东魏 | | 534 – | 549 |
|   Northern Qi | 北齐 | | 550 – | 577 |
|   Northern Zhou | 北周 | | 557 – | 581 |
| **Sui dynasty** | 隋 | | 581 – | 618 |
| **Tang dynasty** | 唐 | | 618 – | 907 |
| **Five dynasties** | 五代 | | 907 – | 960 |
| **Liao dynasty** | 辽 | | 907 – | 1125 |
| **Song dynasty** | 宋 | | 960 – | 1279 |
|   Northern | 北宋 | | 960 – | 1127 |
|   Southern | 南宋 | | 1127 – | 1279 |
| **Jin dynasty** | 金 | | 1115 – | 1234 |

| | | | | |
|---|---|---|---|---|
| Yuan dynasty | 元 | 1279 | – | 1368 |
| Ming dynasty | 明 | 1368 | – | 1644 |
| Hongwu | 洪武 | 1368 | – | 1398 |
| Jianwen | 建文 | 1399 | – | 1402 |
| Yongle | 永乐 | 1403 | – | 1424 |
| Hongxi | 洪熙 | 1425 | | |
| Xuande | 宣德 | 1426 | – | 1435 |
| Zhengtong | 正统 | 1436 | – | 1449 |
| Jingtai | 景泰 | 1450 | – | 1456 |
| Tianshun | 天顺 | 1457 | – | 1464 |
| Chenghua | 成亿 | 1465 | – | 1487 |
| Hongzhi | 弘治 | 1488 | – | 1505 |
| Zhengde | 正德 | 1506 | – | 1521 |
| Jiajing | 嘉靖 | 1522 | – | 1566 |
| Longqing | 隆庆 | 1567 | – | 1572 |
| Wanli | 万历 | 1573 | – | 1620 |
| Taichang | 泰昌 | 1620 | | |
| Tianqi | 天启 | 1621 | – | 1627 |
| Chongzhen | 崇祯 | 1628 | – | 1644 |
| Qing dynasty | 清 | 1644 | – | 1911 |
| Shunzhi | 顺治 | 1644 | – | 1661 |
| Kangxi | 康熙 | 1662 | – | 1722 |
| Yongzheng | 雍正 | 1723 | – | 1735 |
| Qianlong | 乾隆 | 1736 | – | 1795 |
| Jiaqing | 嘉庆 | 1796 | – | 1820 |
| Daoguang | 道光 | 1821 | – | 1850 |
| Xianfeng | 咸丰 | 1851 | – | 1861 |
| Tongzhi | 同治 | 1862 | – | 1874 |
| Guangxu | 光绪 | 1875 | – | 1908 |
| Xuantong | 宣统 | 1909 | – | 1911 |
| Republic of China | 中华民国 | 1911 | – | 1949 |
| People's Republic of China | 中华人民共和国 | 1949 | – | |

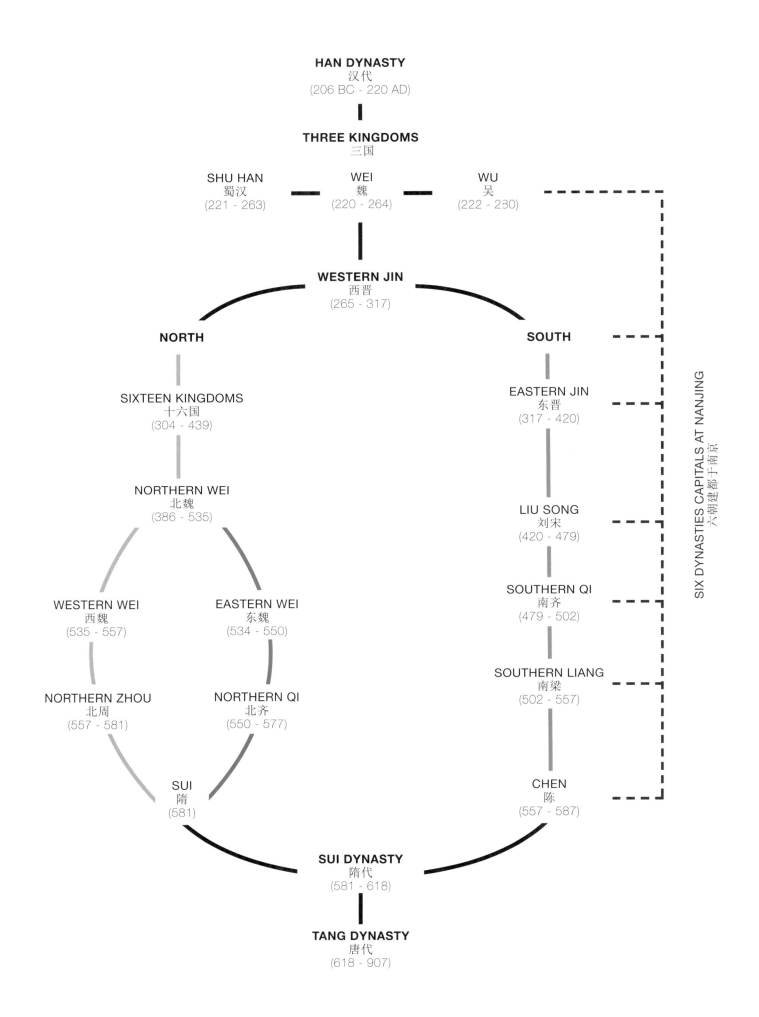

**HAN DYNASTY**
汉代
(206 BC - 220 AD)

**THREE KINGDOMS**
三国

SHU HAN
蜀汉
(221 - 263)

WEI
魏
(220 - 264)

WU
吴
(222 - 230)

**WESTERN JIN**
西晋
(265 - 317)

**NORTH**

**SOUTH**

SIXTEEN KINGDOMS
十六国
(304 - 439)

EASTERN JIN
东晋
(317 - 420)

NORTHERN WEI
北魏
(386 - 535)

LIU SONG
刘宋
(420 - 479)

WESTERN WEI
西魏
(535 - 557)

EASTERN WEI
东魏
(534 - 550)

SOUTHERN QI
南齐
(479 - 502)

NORTHERN ZHOU
北周
(557 - 581)

NORTHERN QI
北齐
(550 - 577)

SOUTHERN LIANG
南梁
(502 - 557)

SUI
隋
(581)

CHEN
陈
(557 - 587)

**SUI DYNASTY**
隋代
(581 - 618)

**TANG DYNASTY**
唐代
(618 - 907)

SIX DYNASTIES CAPITALS AT NANJING
六朝建都于南京

# Northern Dynasties (386 - 581): Sculpture in Turbulent Times
by Annette L. Juliano

## Prologue

For several decades, Norman Kurland has been an ardent and astute collector of ancient Chinese art. He focused primarily on mortuary and Buddhist sculpture, from the Northern Dynasties, late third to late sixth centuries, when north China's fate was controlled by nomadic tribes from the northeast and northwest regions. As a true connoisseur, his intense commitment to grasp more fully the art and culture of the Northern Dynasties inspired the pursuit of two Master's degrees from University of London's School of Oriental and African Studies (SOAS) and another from The Courtauld Institute of Art, studying 'Buddhist Art: History and Conservation.' At the same time, he worked relentlessly to refine his choices, crafting an exceptional collection. Kurland has a passionate connection to Buddhist sculpture from the fifth through late sixth century and to non-Buddhist clay tomb sculpture (*mingqi* 明器), particularly from the sixth century. Like the facets of a prism, the objects in his collection reflect certain fundamental aspects of Northern Dynasties artistic accomplishment and visual culture.

## History of Turbulent Times

Before proceeding to explore the art and culture of the Northern Dynasties, the underlying historical context needs to be briefly recounted. China's first empire, the Han dynasty (206 BCE - 220 CE), initiated an era of unprecedented prosperity. A strong military expanded its external reach into the western regions, beginning the early stages of the overland trade routes later known collectively as the Silk Road. After several centuries, however, the Han Empire crumbled as China became embroiled in devastating civil warfare and nomadic invasions with ephemeral dynasties ruled by Chinese or by various tribes struggling for control of territory (see page 12). Han territory divided into the Three Kingdoms and overlapped briefly in the north and northwest with the Sixteen Kingdoms, only three of which were ruled by Chinese. The Three Kingdoms persisted until the late third century when China was again unified for about fifty-two years by the Western Jin dynasty (265 - 317) which tried to rekindle the former glory of the Han, reviving the ancient capitals of Luoyang 洛阳 and Chang'an 长安 (modern Xi'an 西安). However, in 317, an overwhelming onslaught of invading nomadic horsemen ravaged north China, leaving both venerable imperial capitals, Luoyang and Chang'an, in smoldering ruins; the remnants of the Western Jin court fled the offensive southward. Overcoming the resistance of established southern elite families with the support of fleeing northern émigrés, the Western Jin was renamed the Eastern Jin dynasty (317 - 420) and founded a new capital and imperial court at Jiankang 建康 (modern Nanjing). By the late fourth century, the Tuoba Xianbei 拓拔 鲜卑, a confederation among competing nomadic tribes, emerged victorious, eventually unifying the north under the banner of the Northern Wei dynasty (386 - 535).[1]

## *Northern Wei and the Tuoba Xianbei*

In a divided China, the North was ruled by the nomads and the South by the Chinese, commencing the period identified as the Northern and Southern Dynasties (see page 12 and page 15, map A).[2] The dominant branch of the Xianbei, known as the Tuoba, established an independent state, called the Northern Wei dynasty, in northern Shanxi province in 386 and gradually defeated all rivals; in 398, the first capital was established at Pingcheng 平城 (modern Datong).[3] When Gansu province was annexed in 439, Tuoba Wei succeeded in unifying the North. Control of Gansu gave the Northern Wei rulers even greater access to the western regions. Then, in 493 to 494, Emperor Xiaowen 孝文 moved the capital of the Northern Wei from Pingcheng, close to the Inner Mongolian border and the Xianbei homelands, to the ancient city of Luoyang, the heartland of traditional Han culture, which he had rebuilt.[4] At the new capital, his policy, referred to as sinicization, mandated that Chinese be the official court language and compelled the Tuoba aristocrats to adopt Chinese dress and surnames as well as intermarry with Chinese gentry. By the early sixth century, this policy led to internal tensions and struggles between the ruling house and the opposing tribal aristocracy who resented relinquishing their Tuoba heritage. Power struggles and bloodshed returned to the North. In 535, Northern Wei split into two dynasties, both founded by Xianbei generals (map B). In the West, with Luoyang again in ruins, powerful aristocratic families and military officials regrouped in Chang'an, and General Yuwen Tai 宇文泰 founded the Western Wei dynasty (535 - 557) lasting about twenty years to be replaced again by a Yu family palace coup which formed the Northern Zhou dynasty (557 - 581) (maps B, C). In the East, Gao Huan 高歡 established the Eastern Wei (534 - 550), also lasting some twenty years with a new capital at Ye in southern Hebei province, only to be overthrown again by a Gao family coup forming the Northern Qi dynasty (550 - 577) (maps B, C). Political conflict was no longer north and south but also east and west, as the Northern Zhou and Northern Qi sought to unify the two territories and reunite all of China. However, Yang Jian 杨坚, an eminent statesman and general at the Northern Zhou court, ascended to the throne in 581 and eventually reunified north and south China as Emperor Wendi under the Sui dynasty (581 - 618). Finally, China saw its second great empire reconstituted in the Tang dynasty (618 - 907) enduring for just under three hundred years.

*Perception of the Northern Dynasties*

The collapse of the Han dynasty in 220 CE violated 'the most persistent ideal of Chinese history,' the unity of China.[5] Subsequent Chinese historians saw the dislocation, disorder and bloody court struggles as primarily negative.[6] The division between the North and South represented not only a geographic reality, but also epitomized a divide between the 'civilized' and 'barbaric.'[7] Of course, Southern Dynasties literary sources, such as the *Nan Qi Shu* 南齐书, *History of the Southern Qi Dynasty* or the *Wei Lu Zhuan* 魏虏傳, *Barbarians of Wei* or *Account of the Wei Barbarians*, tended to under-rate the level of Tuoba civilization.[8] The Southern Dynasties had the legitimacy, remaining fiercely loyal to the institution of the emperor as a guardian of the Chinese way of life. Based on very limited information or misinformation and sometimes contradicting descriptions provided in the *Wei Shu* 魏书, *History of the Wei Dynasty*, these Southern Dynasties sources defined the age with epithets such as the 'five barbarian groups brought disorder to China' 五胡乱华. These disparaging descriptions both amplified the cultural superiority of the developed South and reinforced the stereotype of the primitive barbarians (*huren* 胡人) of the North.[9]

Initially, a not dissimilar bias shaped twentieth century scholarship. But twenty years ago, our perception of the Northern and Southern Dynasties period began to shift away from the rather dismissive attitudes of both Western and Chinese scholars, more comfortable among the splendors of the Han and Tang empires.[10] A steady flow of often incredible archaeological discoveries and a veritable explosion of small and large exhibitions in the United States, Europe and Asia fed the fascination with the Silk Road. A growing appreciation of its pivotal role in transmitting culture through commerce during this period generated even more substantial scholarship and intense interest. This was no longer a 'Dark Age' as characterized by some scholars but an era of continuity and discontinuity as the enduring Chinese value system struggled with change, often at a rapid pace in a society with fluid or blurring

boundaries.[11] Finally, the Northern and Southern Dynasties period achieved recognition as being fundamental to the achievements of the Tang empire and later dynasties as well as being itself a dynamic and vigorous epoch in the history of Chinese culture. Archaeological activity continues to yield tomb contents and Buddhist material that enriches our understanding of the North and the South.

Even in this summarized version, the historical overview conveys the complexity of this period and the pivotal role of the nomadic conquerors. Actually, Chinese history can be chronicled not only by the linear rise and fall of dynasty after dynasty but also by the ebb and flow of the periodic encounters between the Central Plains dwellers (Chinese or Han people) and their nomadic neighbors.[12] In fact, almost a third of the dynastic houses that ruled China throughout its long and remarkable history were non-Han peoples (nomads or non-Chinese).[13] The following essay is not intended as a traditional overview of the art historical stylistic developments of the Northern Dynasties but as an opportunity to reconsider the perception and character of Northern Dynasties culture and to contextualize the artistic accomplishments in ceramics, mortuary and Buddhist sculpture as evidenced in the Kurland Collection.

## Distinctive Northern Culture

Spanning some three hundred years under the Northern Dynasties, the artistic production, particularly mortuary and Buddhist sculpture, ceramics and surviving painting, all evidence, to some degree, the enormous diversity of culture at this time. This emerged from the encounters of traditional Han culture of the Central Plains in the North with five sources of influence: the successful invasions and the dominant rule of the Tuoba Xianbei, the arrival of Buddhism and other religions, the network of trade routes, carrying goods, ideas and people from the West into China, regional cultures within north China, and interaction with the Southern Dynasties, recognized as the preservers of Chinese cultural values. The response to these influences manifested in the arts along a spectrum; at one end are the assimilated motifs such as the rich floral vocabulary, palmette designs and scrolls from West Asian and Classical worlds and lotuses from Buddhist art. These largely replaced or coexisted with the familiar Han cloud scrolls as a decorative ground and vocabulary. At the other end of the spectrum, hybridity: Chinese and foreign motifs were juxtaposed, as visible in tomb art, creating a distinctive northern visual culture with intersecting regional artistic styles.[14]

Map A:
Divided China, Northern Wei Dynasty and Southern Dynasties. (Mapping Specialists, Ltd.)

Map B:
Western and Eastern Wei Dynasties and Southern Dynasties. (Mapping Specialists, Ltd.)

Map C:
Northern Zhou and Northern Qi Dynasties and Southern Dynasties. (Mapping Specialists, Ltd.)

15

Fig. 1a, b.
Details of *pushou* carved on two Eastern Han (25 - 220 CE) tomb doors in the Luoyang Museum of Ancient Tombs, Henan.
a. (Photo, Annette Juliano).
b. (Photo, Gary Lee Todd) (Wikimedia Commons: http://picasaweb.google.com/GaryLeeTodd and http://picasaweb.google.com/leefoxx1949/ under the license GFDL 1.3 and CC-by-SA-all).

Fig. 2a, b
Late fifth century CE Northern Wei gilt bronze *pushou*:
a. Detail of space above the mask with 'palmette tree,' Norman A. Kurland Collection. Cat no. 9.
b. Mask from Northern Wei tomb No. 1, Hudong, Datong, Shanxi, (Cultural Relics Press, Wenwu chubanshe文物出版社, Beijing).

Fig. 3
Detail of space above the mask with multi-armed figure, Northern Wei bronze *pushou*, Norman A. Kurland Collection. Cat. no. 8.

## Pushou, Palmettes and other Foreign Motifs

The Kurland Collection includes three late fifth century, originally gilt bronze, *pushou* 铺首, animal or monster masks, a matching pair with ring handles and a single example missing the ring. The collection also includes two glazed Northern Qi ceramics, an earthenware vase and a spherical green vase. Both vessels display applied embellishments which epitomize this interplay or dialogue between traditional Chinese artistry and the influx of non-Chinese motifs described above (cat. nos. 8, 9, 30, 31). Typically, *pushou* consist of a large monster head with bulging eyes, triangular nose with flared nostrils, a mouth ring flanked by teeth and two formidable fangs that protrude from the mouth; above the eyes there can be a variety of motifs. Such monster or animal plaques with ring handles have a long history reaching back to Western Zhou bronze vessels; in the Warring States period, bronze *pushou* were affixed to outer wooden coffins, *guo* 椁, as symbolic handles. Carved in stone on Han tomb doors, *pushou* appear with three triangular forms atop of the mask, perhaps a center crest and two horns or ears (figs. 1a, b). However, in the Northern Dynasties, particularly during the Northern Wei in the late fifth century, gilt-bronze versions, mostly from wooden coffins, display a substantial change in motifs and iconography, splendidly represented on the three Kurland *pushou* (cat. nos. 8, 9). On the pair, the space above the animal mask is filled with a central crest formed by a five-petal palmette, almost like a tree, and two curved horns, while the larger single *pushou* has a four or possibly six-armed female deity grasping the necks of two lion-like heads with elongated snake bodies (figs. 2a, 3).[15] Similar *pushou* with palmettes or figures and the same configuration of motifs have been found across the northern corridor of China in the late fifth century, in Guyuan, Ningxia, Datong, Shanxi and Inner Mongolia (fig. 5).[16]

Many *pushou* (including an attached ring) from this northern corridor have human figures grasping Chinese dragons or other less identifiable animals, others are embellished with vegetation or curled horns; images of humans grasping the necks of confronted animals trace back to art of the Ancient Near East, with symbolism suggesting a 'Master or Lord of the Animals,' who controls the animal world, a motif which probably arrived in China through Bactria and Gandhara.[17] All four sides of late fifth century Song Shaozu's 宋绍祖 stone sarcophagus from Datong, including the tomb door and its lunette, have *pushou* carved in raised relief on their surfaces (fig. 4a).[18] On this sarcophagus, the *pushou* have palmettes, an *apsaras* 天人 and voluptuous females like those in the 'inhabited vine' motif found on the carved stone plinth (fig. 4b) in the tomb of Sima Jinlong 司马金龙 (d. 484) and in Yungang's 云岗 Cave X, both in Datong.[19] An example excavated from a tomb in Guyuan,

Fig. 4a, b
a. Female figure holding the monster's horns, in space above the mask, from a *pushou* carved on the surface of Song Shaozu's sandstone sarcophagus, dated 477 CE. Caofulou Village, Datong, Shanxi. (Photo, Annette Juliano).
b. Rubbing from stone plinth carved with an 'inhabited vine,' voluptuous figures sitting in palmette vines, from tomb of Sima Jinlong, (d. 484), Prince of Langya, Datong, Shanxi. (Photo, Annette Juliano).

Fig. 5
Bronze *pushou*, one of a pair, with traces of gilt, from Northern Wei tomb (late fifth century), excavated from Leizumiao Village, western suburbs of Guyuan, Ningxia. Small figures hold animal necks but probably represent the Infant Buddha. Guyuan Municipal Museum, Ningxia Hui Autonomous Region, Courtesy of Luo Feng, Director, Ningxia Institute of Archaeology and Cultural Relics, Yinchuan, Ningxia Hui Autonomous Region.

Fig. 6a, b
a. Earthenware jar with applied, molded relief decoration under brown greenish glaze, Northern Qi dynasty (550 - 577), Norman A. Kurland Collection. Cat. no. 31.
b. Molded appliqué ornament of moustached face. Khotanese earthenware. The State Hermitage Museum, St. Petersburg.

Ningxia, shows a representation of the Infant Buddha in the space above the mask and in the suspended ring (fig. 5). The outer edge of the ring also bears raptor-like birds similar to those found on nomadic metalwork in Inner Mongolia.[20]

Certainly, the low-fired, glazed earthenware jar in the Kurland Collection from the Northern Qi dynasty (550 - 577) displays a stunning mélange of external motifs stamped separately and applied to the surface of a standard Chinese *hu* 壺 jar, including a pearl roundel filled with a Central Asian mustached face, palmettes and other decorative appliqués (cat. no. 31, fig. 6a). Direct parallels for many of these motifs can be found among the earthenware appliqués at Yotkan, the ancient capital of the Kingdom of Khotan, at the southern rim of Taklamakan in Xinjiang, dated 1st - 3rd century CE. (fig. 6a, b).[21] The exquisitely balanced spherical-shaped green splash-glazed jar with a cover has seven applied oval medallions, each with a pearl border enclosing a musician or dancer (cat. no. 30, fig. 7). The pearl bordered medallions became a widespread decorative motif across Central Asia visible on Buddhist sculpture as early as the mid-fifth century and intensely popular by the mid-sixth century.

*First Northern Wei Capital: Pingcheng*

Since the Eastern Han dynasty (25 - 220 CE), the Tuoba had been living along the northern border of China, within the northern loop of the Yellow River and in Inner Mongolia and from this proximity acquired familiarity with characteristics of the Chinese civilian and military way of life. The Tuoba Xianbei armies, particularly their powerful cavalry, supported the tribe's successful expansion into the Central Plains; by 439, the Tuoba Xianbei armies conquered Gansu and the Northern Wei dynasty gained control of all the North.[22] During their expansion into the 'heartland' of China, Tuoba leaders sought to consolidate their military victory by ruling the empire with the support and the talents of educated Chinese officials. They became increasingly reliant on a Chinese-style bureaucracy.[23] This created a culture and society of interdependence between the non-Chinese and Han China, beginning the complex process of acculturation.

In 398, the first of two Northern Wei capitals was established by Tuoba Gui at Pingcheng 平城, which sits in the far north of Shanxi province several miles from the Inner Mongolia border, just inside the Great Wall nearer to the Xianbei homeland and grazing areas. Envisioning a great capital city, he ordered half a million people forcibly resettled in the city and its vicinity, including 100,000 skilled artisans from the east along with other non-Chinese.[24] After the conquest of Gansu, the population of the city of Guzang 姑臧 (modern

Wuwei, formerly the capital of Northern Liang, 398 - 439) was forced to evacuate the city and migrate from the west to resettle in Pingcheng, bringing more artistic talent and the Buddhist religious zeal of local and foreign monks. *Wei Shu* 魏书 *History of the Wei Dynasty* recounts that 'when the Liang population was transferred to the capital, the monks came eastward with their Buddhist paraphernalia, and "teaching by images" spread far and wide.'[25] The location of Gansu, situated where the Silk Routes funnel into China, facilitated frequent contact with western artisans and missionaries, encouraging imitation of foreign models to create images for this new foreign religion, Buddhism, spreading in China.[26] The Tuoba enthusiastically adopted and patronized Buddhism earlier and more universally than the Chinese, even in the North.[27]

Tuoba Gui conceived of Pingcheng, his first formal capital, as a grand imperial city and immediately initiated major construction works: major Buddhist temple complexes, monks' quarters, a five-story pagoda, palaces, ancestral temples, altars to soil and grain and ritual buildings including a *mingtang*. At its peak from the 430s to 470s, Pingcheng became a true imperial enclave, its palaces, parks, pools and residences restricted to the Tuoba and their officials, some of whom were undoubtedly Chinese. The city plan reflected the Tuoba rulers' awareness of basic features of Chinese imperial cities. At the same time, Pingcheng was a hybrid city with designated areas beyond the city and palace walls of 'yurt cities,' accommodating traditional nomadic lifestyles. Pingcheng, an active trade hub with merchants and missions arriving from Central Asia, Ferghana, Kashmir, Persia, and Koguryo, was also a center of Buddhism, with perhaps 100 Buddhist establishments and some 2,000 monks or nuns in residence.[28] Recent excavations of Pingcheng which lies beneath the modern city of Datong have confirmed the grandeur described in the *Wei Shu*.[29] These contradict to a degree the impression conveyed by envoys from the Southern Dynasties (*Song Shu* 宋书, Liu Song dynasty 刘宋, 420 - 479) who saw only 'a thin Chinese veneer over what must have seemed to them sheer barbarism.'[30]

*Yungang and Fifth Century Buddhist Sculpture*

Ten miles west of Pingcheng, one of the most famous rock cut cave temples, Yungang, was opened in the mid-fifth century. The continuing research at existing Buddhist cave sites, as well as newly discovered caves and cache burials of hundreds of Buddhist images do not in any way diminish the importance of Yungang's contribution to fifth century Buddhist imagery. The first five imperial caves scooped out of the sandstone cliff, Numbers XVI - XX and two smaller but still monumental paired chambers VII - VIII and IX - X

Fig. 7
Spherical green-glazed jar with seven applied medallions each with pearl borders and molded reliefs of Central Asian musicians playing transverse flutes or lutes and dancers. Northern Qi dynasty (550 - 577), Norman A. Kurland Collection. Cat. no. 30.

Fig. 8
Seated cross-legged Shakyamuni Buddha, Cave XX, Yungang Grottoes, outside Datong, Shanxi, carved into a sandstone cliff, dated to the 460s. (Photo, Annette Juliano).

Fig. 9
Head of bodhisattva from Cave XVIII,
Yungang Grottoes, outside Datong, Shanxi;
crown shows penetration of motifs from
West Asia: pearl borders, palmettes, and
disk and crescent. (Photo, Annette Juliano).

Fig. 10a, b
a. Sandstone *apsaras*
(heavenly being) floating
through the air holding a
bowl in the raised hand;
from the style, carving,
and stone, most likely from
Yungang grottoes, Norman
A. Kurland Collection.
b. Head of clay tomb figure
of a Xianbei from Sima
Jinlong's tomb (d. 484),
Datong, Shanxi. Facial
features of the *apsaras* and
the Xianbei are remarka-
bly similar, (Cultural Relics
Press, Wenwu chubanshe文
物出版社, Beijing).

were completed mostly in the 460s and 470s.[31]
The five imperial caves each have a massive,
southward facing central Buddha image nearly
filling the shallow oval spaces. Numbers XX
and XVII remain the most compelling in their
monumental simplicity and sculptural presence.
Tanyao, a monk from Gansu, persuaded the
emperor to support this project as atonement for
his predecessor's paranoid persecution of the
Buddhists and as a symbol of Northern Wei power.
The Tuoba rulers' adoption and sponsorship of
Buddhism, a foreign religion to both the non-
Chinese and Chinese, helped unify the empire and
gave the Northern Wei greater legitimacy, merging
political and religious power.

Cave XX's forty foot seated Buddha and Cave
XVIII's fifty-one foot standing image convey a
sense of monumentality and expansive energy
(fig. 8). Framed on either side by large elongated
ears and capped with smooth hair and *ushnisha*,
their full faces with sharply chiseled features and
a characteristic 'archaic smile' combine strength
and magnanimity. The configuration of the
robes, decorative borders, palmette vines, and
bodhisattvas' crowns reflect the overwhelmingly
Western orientation, with sculptural elements
for the most part Central Asian, Mathuran and
Gandharan (figs. 8, 9). However, the images
show a transcendent synthesis, more than merely
copying. As Dr. Alexander C. Soper has pointed
out, there are no exact prototypes and no written
proof of the participation of foreign craftsmen
or monk supervisors. 'It is likely that western
precedents were transmitted by small portable
images, paintings or iconographic pattern-books'
– perhaps supplemented by vague descriptions of
travelers.[32]

Among the Buddhist images Kurland assembled
are five fifth century examples that provide insight
into early image making both in stone and bronze,
that not only depended largely on foreign models
but also resonated with the Yungang style. Both
sandstone pieces, an *apsaras* and the remaining
head and shoulders of a Buddha (fig. 10a and
cat. no. 4), most likely came from Yungang and
probably date from the late fifth century, 480s and
490s. Usually carved into the upper or heavenly
register of the cave, the *apsaras*, *tianren* 天人 or
heavenly beings, swoop through the air trailing
scarves, carrying offerings and attending the
deities. Although without scarves, the Kurland
*apsaras* firmly grasps and raises a bowl probably
filled with fruit; simply carved, the figure conveys
a gentle elegance. Interestingly, the small features
centered in a broad full face resembles the faces
of Xianbei as captured in the clay tomb figures
furnishing the tomb of Sima Jinlong (d. 484),
unearthed in Datong (fig. 10b).[33] The other Kurland
piece, the upper part of a Buddha (a bust), seems
to reflect late fifth century changes visible in the
proportions of the head and more elongated form,

conveying more Chinese features.

Each of the three bronze Buddhas seated on Mount Sumeru-shaped thrones is draped with the 'open mode' style of robe which partially bares the right shoulder and reveals the undergarment diagonally across the chest; the edges of the undergarment and sometimes the robe itself have pearl borders, an ubiquitous motif from Central Asia (cat. nos. 2, 3, figs. 8, 11, 12 and 13). Two of the three show the edge of the robe draping down the proper left shoulder forming a zigzag of overlapping folds. The general configuration of the Buddha's drapery and the articulation of the folds of the robe visible on these three fifth-century bronze images echo the major stylistic characteristics of the five earliest caves at Yungang. The square bronze plaque framed by a pearl border reiterates the central Buddha's connection to Yungang: the flanking bodhisattvas; a canopy; and *apsaras* which have distinctly non-Chinese faces and Indian iconographic details such as diagonally crossing chains of jewelry (fig. 13). The gilt bronze seated Shakyamuni, dated 482 of the Taihe 太和 era or last quarter of the fifth century, is a fine example of the impressive gilt bronze images produced in Hebei and Shanxi during this time (cat. no. 2, fig. 11); the throne is embellished with vegetal and palmette scrolls and lotus petals that become a mainstay of the Chinese decorative vocabulary.

*Second Northern Wei Capital: Luoyang*

Emperor Xiaowen 孝文帝 ruled Northern Wei from 471 - 499, at first from Pingcheng. In 493 - 4, he transferred the capital to Luoyang 洛阳, Henan, reviving the ancient imperial city and filling it with about half a million people from Pingcheng. Emperor Xiaowen was famous for promoting and implementing the provocative policy of sinification.[34] After the move to Luoyang, Emperor Xiaowen adopted the Chinese language at court, banning all non-Chinese languages. He demanded that all courtiers wear Chinese clothes and acquire Chinese names. This policy shift was not necessarily instigated by a desire to become Chinese but served to legitimize Tuoba nomadic rule after the Chinese imperial model by centralizing more power, by pushing acculturation to minimize conflicts between non-Chinese and Chinese and thus making it easier to rule a multi-ethnic society.[35] Tuoba elite at the Luoyang court did not become 'replicas' of the Chinese elite. These policies supported the emergence of a new hybrid elite, mixing Chinese and Xianbei characteristics through intermarriage of Tuoba royalty to Chinese, and giving equal office holding status and titles at court. Sino-Xianbei intermarriages were a decisive factor in forging hybrid elite families that would later be fundamental to the reunified Sui and Tang dynasties' societies.[36]

Fig. 11
Seated gilt-bronze of Shakyamuni, dated 482, with visible elements of Yungang style and the palmette scrolls and lotus petals integrated into the Chinese Buddhist and decorative vocabulary, Norman A. Kurland Collection. Cat. no. 2.

Fig. 12a, b
a. Small bronze image of Maitreya seated on a Mount Sumeru throne; pearl border on the edges of the robe and undergarment and twisted rope patterned around the edge of the throne.
b. Detail of twisted rope pattern on edge of throne, Norman A. Kurland Collection. Cat. no. 3.

Fig. 13
Bronze plaque with Buddha seated on a Mount Sumeru throne, Norman A. Kurland Collection.

Fig. 14
Longmen Grottoes, carved from limestone cliffs, outside Luoyang, Henan; Central Binyang cave, main Buddha image dated 523; mature Northern Wei style with cascade of drapery, front view and side view. (Photos, Annette Juliano).

However, relocating the capital south to Luoyang and the increasing Chinese orientation of the emperor and the court were resisted by a faction of the Tuoba which eventually contributed to the downfall of the dynasty.

Like Tuoba Gui at Pingcheng, Emperor Xiaowen had very ambitious plans, rapidly rebuilding this ancient imperial city under continued imperial direction. Luoyang did not evolve naturally; its entire character was formed under the supervision of the emperor but took twenty years to complete under several later emperors. Contemporary descriptions of Luoyang suggest its original magnificence with palaces, pagodas and monasteries. Apparently, gardens were also built by the imperial family, wealthy commoners and Buddhist temple officials. *The Record of the Buddhist Monasteries of Lo-yang* by Yang Hsüan-chih describes more than twenty gardens that recreate visions of mountain valleys and Buddhist paradises with ponds, exotic plants, fruits and song birds as well as cicadas.[37] The inner walled city was restricted to palaces, civil and Buddhist structures, while the rest was divided into walled wards, following the grid designed by Emperor Xiaowen's planners.[38] The eastern district was primarily residential with a market; the north was largely an open space for training the military; a large residential foreign community, perhaps as many as fifty thousand, was segregated to the south and also sheltered foreign visitors and immigrants; the western district was restricted to imperial families and their relatives, monasteries, another market, shopkeepers, and even entertainers. The most lucrative economic activity in the city was the importation and sale of luxury and exotic goods from abroad.[39]

Just after the move from Pingcheng, Emperor Xiaowen (also known after his death as Gaozu) ordered that no monasteries could be built in Luoyang apart from the famous wooden Yongning 永宁塔 pagoda and nunnery in the inner city, a prohibition that was flouted after his death.[40] Only after most of Luoyang was completed did later rulers and the elite turn their wealth and energy to the construction of monasteries and temples. Religious enthusiasm permeated the city which eventually boasted over one thousand structures. There were many festivals and splendid processions in which Buddha figures were carried through the streets with acrobats and musicians to celebrate Shakyamuni's birthday as well as other events.[41]

*Longmen Cave Temples and Early Sixth Century Buddhist Sculpture*

To commemorate his father, Emperor Xiaowen sponsored the opening of the Central Binyang Cave 賓阳窟 in hard limestone cliffs twelve

Fig. 15a, b
a. Fully developed Northern Wei Buddhist style with slender body and cascades of drapery, Norman A. Kurland. Cat. no. 26.
b. A standing gilt bronze Guanyin, dated by inscription to 516, with distinctive Northern Wei sharp angular 'fish tail' drapery, Norman A. Kurland Collection. Cat. no. 13.

kilometers (7.5 miles) south of Luoyang in what was called the Longmen Grottoes 龙门石窟 or Dragon Gate Grottoes. Finished in 523, this cave and its carved images of Buddhas, monks, and bodhisattvas are celebrated for their distinctive Northern Wei sculptural style dated to the first quarter of the sixth century. Although this style emerges in the late fifth century, visible in Yungang Cave VI, it reaches its apogee in the Binyang Cave. The new sculptural concept de-emphasizes the body which recedes under a complex pattern of rhythmic pleating in the skirt, robes and shawl. This style of dress is referred to as *baoyi bodai* 褒衣博带, 'loose robe, wide girdle,' a loose outer robe with wide sleeves that hangs open at the front, showing the undergarment with a sash tied just above the waist (fig. 14).[42] This configuration of garments was actually a reinterpretation of the Buddhist robe, mixing Chinese and Indian elements.[43] The complex cascade of drapery draws attention away from the body, and the head and hands of the Buddha form a crucial visual triangular focus.

Four small sculptures in the Kurland Collection, two limestone and two bronze, capture the intense linearity and compelling spiritual presence of this highly distinctive style (cat. nos. 13, 26, fig. 15a, b). In particular, the two bronze images, one seated dated 539 and the other standing and extensively gilded dated 516, reflect a more exaggerated version of this Northern Wei style, with the body engulfed by the cascading drapery laid out symmetrically, becoming increasingly angular at the bottom (figs. 15a, b). The standing gilt bronze Guanyin has drapery and shawls that splay out on either side of the legs, radiating energy outward and upward to the pointed flame-shaped mandorla (fig. 15b). This innovative stylistic idiom dominated and shaped both Buddhist imagery and clay tomb sculpture from the Luoyang area during the first quarter of the sixth century. The superb mastery shown here and in the elegantly articulated clay tomb sculpture from the early sixth century in the Kurland Collection reflects the best of this sculptural concept and underscores the stylistic interaction between Buddhist and non-Buddhist art.[44]

These dramatic changes in the character of Buddhist sculpture are usually attributed to influence from the highly sophisticated Chinese craftsmen of the Southern Dynasties, reflected in the images found in Chengdu, Sichuan, dated as early at 483. This idea was first developed in the 1960s by Soper and has continued to be debated for over fifty years.[45] However, regardless of whether powerful stimuli from the South contributed to the development of northern sculpture, what emerged in the North was a synthesis of influences, creating a singular style.

**Fig. 16**
Caparisoned horse, usually considered the 'riderless' representation of the deceased in funerary procession, earthenware with pigments; Northern Wei, first quarter of the sixth century, Norman A. Kurland Collection. Cat. no. 23.

**Fig. 17a, b**
a. Clay tomb figure of military honor guard from first quarter of the sixth century, reflecting flat elegant style of the Luoyang area, Norman A. Kurland Collection.
b. Clay tomb figure with glaze, of military man with helmet from tomb of Sima Jinlong (d. 484), Shanxi Province Datong, (Cultural Relics Press, Wenwu chubanshe文物出版社, Beijing).

## 'Luoyang' Style Early Sixth Century Clay Tomb Sculpture

One of the core strengths of the Kurland Collection is its superb clay tomb sculpture dating from the first quarter of the sixth century and sharing analogous stylistic features with the Buddhist sculpture discussed above. From the archaeological record to date, comparable examples have been found largely in the Luoyang area. Regrettably, clay tomb sculpture, perhaps with the exception of that from Tang, has held an ambiguous position in the hierarchy of Chinese sculpture, considered more as sociological or anthropological documentation rather than being granted artistic validity. The beauty of many of the examples in the Kurland Collection challenges this notion. Military and civilian honor guards here are represented with elongated and flattened bodies, almost two-dimensional with low relief and fine linear, symmetrical articulation of detail; two have exceptionally tall attenuated forms creating supremely elegant figures. These military officials, in particular, emphasize frontality and symmetry, with small facial features whose introspective smiles convey the solemnity and dignity almost of an icon (cat. no. 10). The fifteen seated musicians in the collection (cat. no. 15), as well as the twins (cat. no. 11) all have enigmatic half-smiles; interestingly, shield-carrying warriors, perhaps mythical, and foreigners from the West with non-Chinese faces have large noses, deep-set eyes and, often, beards. However, all models, including the dogs, oxen, horses and ungainly camels standing on spindly legs and lifting their heads high on majestically long, blade-shaped necks convey variations of these distinctive sculptural qualities. One of the masterpieces of what can be called this 'Luoyang style' is the spirited and handsomely caparisoned riderless horse which symbolized the deceased in funeral processions; the magnificent example in the Kurland Collection has the characteristic taut arched neck which tapers to a sharp blade-like edge and ends in a long narrow head (cat. no. 23, fig. 16); executed in low relief, the richly varied textures of horse trappings heighten the elegance of the graceful form without diminishing its sense of vigor.[46]

This shift in the conception of the clay tomb sculpture can be readily grasped by comparing the late fifth century examples from burials around Datong and those of the early sixth century from the Luoyang area (fig. 17a, b).[47] As discussed earlier, elements of this style-change in Buddhist images began to emerge in Yungang Cave VI from the 480s and 490s and became fully developed in the first quarter of the sixth century in Longmen and at the smaller cave temple of Gongxian 鞏縣 as well as in small, portable bronze and stone images. However, its manifestation in clay tomb figures seems to have happened after the move to the new capital, Luoyang, likely inspired by the Buddhist forms.

*Collapse of Northern Wei, Revitalized Xianbei Rule, and Eastern Wei Buddhist Sculpture*

The Northern Wei ruling house suffered rebellions at the garrisons which sparked other uprisings throughout the North, eventually dividing the northern territory into two dynasties. To the West, there were the short lived dynasties, the Western Wei (535 - 557) followed by the Northern Zhou (557 - 581) and their counterparts to the East, the Eastern Wei (534 - 550) and the Northern Qi (550 - 577) (see maps B, C). Both regimes in the East, controlled by the Gao family, epitomized military dynasticism and reasserted Xianbei customs and language.[48] Kurland focused his collecting attention primarily on the richness of the Buddhist sculptural tradition of Eastern Wei and Northern Qi, complemented with a few choice examples of clay tomb sculptures. There are two Eastern Wei Buddhist pieces, a fragment and a bejeweled standing bodhisattva; the fragment preserves the upper right side of a mandorla dated by inscriptions to 536 (fig. 18). Three complete music-playing *apsaras* survive intact with part of a fourth; they demonstrate the continuities as well as the incipient changes of style and iconography from Northern Wei to Eastern Wei. The scarves of the swooping *apsaras* still retain the linear energy of the Northern Wei drapery; however, they have more substantial sculptural bodies (fig. 18).

The second Eastern Wei sculpture is similar to several sculptures in the Qingzhou finds, a carefully buried hoard of Buddhist sculpture from the Qingzhou region of Shandong province. [49,50] It is a beautiful standing bejeweled bodhisattva, unfortunately missing hands and feet (cat. no. 27, figs. 19a, 20a). Two fascinating features, among others visible on this bodhisattva, reflect the cosmopolitan atmosphere of the Ye capital and other northern cities. The first is the thick strands of linked beads laden with medallions, pendants, and cabochons interspersed with an occasional piece of coral; these diagonally crossed chains of jewelry recall Indian prototypes. Similar linked beads can be seen in the lighter, more delicate versions of jewelry painted around the neck of the Bodhisattva Avalokitesvara (Guanyin 观音) in Ajanta Cave 1, dating from the fifth to sixth century (fig. 19b).[51] The second remarkable feature is the representation of pieces of branch coral which was considered a symbol of the luxurious life in China and fetched high prices in Gupta India. Coral most likely reached China during the Northern Dynasties over the land route from India through Central Asia possibly via Iran (fig. 20a).[52] To date, similar representations of coral in bodhisattva jewelry have been found in Northern Qi, on other bodhisattvas, and in beaded strands on a Northern Wei

Fig. 18
Limestone fragment of mandorla with three *apsaras*, remains of pigments and traces of gold foil; dated by inscription to 536, Eastern Wei dynasty (534 - 550), Norman A. Kurland Collection.

Fig. 19a, b
a. Standing bodhisattva with missing hands and feet, with typical stylistic features found at the site of Qingzhou and displaying distinctive beads incorporated into the long jeweled strings, Eastern Wei dynasty (534 - 550), Norman A. Kurland Collection. Cat. no. 27.
b. Detail of similar beads in the necklace painted on the Avalokitesvara on the wall in Ajanta Cave 1, dated to 500. (Open source: The Yorck Project, Indischer Maler des 7 Jahrhunderts-001.jpg).

Fig. 20a, b
a. Eastern Wei dynasty (534 - 550) bodhisattva with branch coral incorporated in long jeweled strings of beads, Norman A. Kurland Collection. Cat. no. 27.
b. Simulated precious coral also found in long strings of beads visible on the early sixth century seated Maitreya in Cave 142, Maijishan Grottoes, southern Gansu, (Cultural Relics Press, Wenwu chubanshe文物出版社, Beijing).

Fig. 21
Bust of a Buddha reflecting the strong influence during the Northern Qi (550 - 577) of the Gupta style. Detail of the Buddha's hair in the 'snail shell curls' typical of the Gupta style. Norman A. Kurland Collection.

bodhisattva in Cave 142 from the Maijishan Cave Temples 麦积山 in southern Gansu (fig. 20b).[53]

The Eastern Wei Buddhist sculptures and the three Northern Qi Buddhas discussed below convey an essential characteristic of Northern Dynasties Buddhist art, its integration of the continuing flow of influences arriving from West Asia, Southeast Asia and India by land and by sea, as well as from regional styles in the North from the neighboring Western Wei and Northern Zhou dynasties and from the Southern Dynasties. Although turmoil in the oasis kingdoms of Central Asia periodically disrupted the overland routes through Gansu, diplomats, merchants, and missionaries resumed their activities by the mid-sixth century as the Turks increased their sovereignty over Central Asia. Northern cities, such as Tianshui 天水 in Gansu, Chang'an in Shaanxi, and Guyuan in Ningxia saw growing colonies of foreign traders living in their midst.[54] The Northern Qi capital of Ye 邺 also had a resident foreign population, apparently with large numbers of Indians and Persians, and foreign goods were in great demand. Jiankang (modern Nanjing), capital of the Southern Dynasties, was also a key port for import and export of goods as well as distribution since commodities and people could easily move along the region's river system.[55]

*Northern Qi Buddhist Sculpture and the Indian Gupta Style (300 - 600)*

Both Buddhist and non-Buddhist Northern Qi sculpture break from any remaining links to the linearity and weightlessness of the Northern Wei sculptural forms; the body emphatically emerges from the cascades of layered drapery. The three Buddhas in the Kurland Collection reflect the brilliant adaptation of the powerful influence of the Indian Gupta style (300 - 600), that clearly entered China along with luxury goods during this period. Exquisitely modeled, the gently rounded body forms are revealed through the thin clinging robes that remained simple and uncluttered with few drapery folds that convey a subdued sensuality (cat. nos. 29 and 37). The third Buddha shows the characteristic Gupta elements: hair articulated with snail shell curls, thin lotus petal shaped eyes, inward gaze and sensitively modeled, full, almost voluptuous, lips, forming an enigmatic smile. With only the head and upper chest preserved, this bust of Buddha is still among the most beautiful Northern Qi Buddhist sculptures, wrapped, as it is, in an aura of singular ethereal elegance that projects an utterly absorbing spiritual presence (fig. 21). Gupta influence penetrated into China not only across Central Asian land routes but also, and, more likely, by the maritime route, through the main entrepot of Jiankang (modern Nanjing). In addition to the pronounced Gupta aesthetic, Northern Qi sculpture reflects the highly diverse artistic environment with motifs adapted from an extraordinary range of cultural sources and shared across different media and contexts, such as glass, metalwork and ceramics as well as tomb wall paintings and stone funerary sarcophagi.

*Northern Qi Clay Tomb Sculpture*

Northern Qi tomb sculptures in the Kurland Collection, particularly the caparisoned horses and the ox, display lively and robust forms enhanced by color and by appliqué details (cat. nos. 34, 38, fig. 23c). The horned ox retains detailed painted eyes framed by rolled eyelids above and eyelashes below (fig. 22). Features and form animate the head and entire body which shares the vitality of the painted animal at the north end of the ceiling of Luo Rui's Northern Qi tomb, southern suburb of Taiyuan, Shanxi.[56] The three decorative straps crossing the ox's back terminate in leonine heads framed with beaded borders and with tassels issuing from the open mouths (fig. 23a). This same motif is seen in many contexts in Northern Qi including the rump of the single Kurland clay horse and a fierce bronze leonine mask also in the Kurland Collection (fig. 23b, c); this type of lion head is found on the shields of clay tomb guardians who often have lions atop of their helmets as well. They refer back to the Greek mythological figure of Heracles; iconographic details of the head, the lion skin and the club travel in various iterations from the Mediterranean region through Afghanistan and northern India across Central Asia to western and then central China.[57]

## Concluding Remarks

As noted earlier, this essay is intended not as a comprehensive, chronological, art historical, or stylistic survey of the entire Kurland Collection but rather as an endeavor to reframe the perception of the Northern Dynasties' artistic achievements through selected individual objects and groups of objects in a historical context. Even amidst continued turmoil, a multi-dimensional culture flourished during the Northern Dynasties. The diversity and richness evident in the arts was spurred by a remarkable fluidity or 'permeability' of cultural boundaries, related in part to shifting degrees of acculturation between the 'Han Chinese' and the Tuoba Xianbei and to northern interactions with the Southern Dynasties. There was also broad exposure and receptiveness to a veritable potpourri of external influences, particularly Buddhism, its works, and paraphernalia arriving in China via overland Silk, steppe and maritime routes. Such intense cross fertilization nourished the distinctive Northern Dynasties aesthetic which eventually assimilated into the Tang dynasty empire's artistic achievements.

The truly startling range, quantity and quality of these new archaeological finds, for example the extraordinary hoard of Buddhist sculpture in the Qingzhou area of Shandong, the Shi Jun sarcophagus, excavated in Chang'an and dated 571, with its Sogdian and Chinese inscription, the magnificent horse paintings preserved on the walls of Luo Rui's tomb in Taiyuan and the exotic foreign metalwork, jewelry and glass buried in elite tombs, force a further reassessment of the Northern Dynasties' contributions to the art and culture of China. This continuing flow of new archaeological information and mounting scholarship have elevated the stature of the Northern and Southern Dynasties to truly transformative.[58]

Norman Kurland has validated his personal passion and his vision by committing to Northern Dynasties sculpture; when he began his collecting journey with Northern Wei clay tomb sculpture, this material lacked the cachet and widespread popularity of Tang *sancai* or three-color glaze tomb sculpture. His choices as a collector offer us an exceptionally revealing window into the achievements of this collector and the complexities and artistic achievements of the Northern Dynasties.

Fig. 22
Clay model of an ox, powerfully modeled and enlivened by the surviving paint in and around the eyes,
Northern Qi (550 - 577), Norman A. Kurland Collection. Cat. no. 38.

Fig. 23a, b, c
a. Detail of the lion head enclosed in a beaded border and hanging from a strap on the ox's rump.
Clay with extensive pigment and remains of gilding, Norman A. Kurland Collection. Cat. no. 38.
b. Bronze lion mask, Norman A. Kurland Collection.
c. Clay model of a caparisoned horse, Northern Qi (550 - 577), Norman A. Kurland Collection.

# Notes

1 Although this is changing, the Xianbei, despite their importance in Chinese history, remain relatively unknown in English language scholarship. But see Charles Holcombe's study, 'The Xianbei in Chinese History,' *Early Medieval China* 19 (2013), p. 1.

2 The appropriate name for the 400-year period between the Han and Tang empires continues to bedevil scholars and remains confusing to the non-specialist. The extensive disunity and political shifts leave largely unsatisfactory choices: 'Three Kingdoms, Western Jin, the Northern and Southern Dynasties period,' 'Three-Kingdoms-Six Dynasties,' or the shorthand version, 'Six Dynasties.' This epithet, simply 'Six Dynasties' period refers to the Wu Kingdom plus the five dynasties, all with their capitals at Jiankang (modern Nanjing). These six dynasties were ruled by Chinese and considered the only legitimate standard bearers of the Han traditions since the North was ruled by 'barbarians.' Western historians some forty years ago were tempted to identify these years as China's 'Dark Ages.' Today, historians often refer to this politically complex span as Early Medieval China which I am reluctant to use since it implies parallels to western history.

3 The name 'Xianbei' itself is a modern standard pronunciation of the two characters, 鲜卑, determined by early Chinese scholars who transcribed the word and not the original native name. More recently, scholars have attempted to reconstruct the native original which sounds something like 'Särbi,' which can only be conjecture. Holcombe, 'The Xianbei', p. 3.

4 See an article by Mark Elliott, '*Hushuo*, The Northern Other and the Naming of the Han Chinese,' p. 174, in *Critical Han Studies, The History and Representation and Identity of China's Majority*, edited by Thomas S. Mullaney, James Leibold, Stephane Gros, and Eric Vanden Bussche (Berkeley, Los Angeles, and London: University of California Press, 2012). He investigates the history and use of the term Han and how it came to be applied to the people of the Central Plains.

5 Scott Pearce, Audrey Spiro and Patricia Ebrey, editors. *Culture and Power in the Reconstitution of the Chinese Realm* (Cambridge, MA. and London: Harvard University Asia Center and distributed by Harvard University Press, 2001): Introduction, p. 1.

6 Ibid.

7 Ibid. Introduction, pp. 18-19.

8 Lou Lin, 'A Study of the Civilization of the Northern Wei Dynasty in its Founding Period,' *Eurasian Studies*, English Edition IV, editors-in-chief, Yu Taishan & Lin Jinxiu (Asia Publishing Nexus, 2016), pp. 95-97. Liu Zhi 劉陟 created a biography of imperial minions (56 *Xingchen Zhuan* 倖臣傳), with a chapter about the 'Barbarians of Wei' (57 *Wei Lu Zhuan* 魏虜傳), the Northern Wei dynasty 北魏 (386 - 534).

9 Ibid., p. 101 and Elliott, '*Hushuo*', p. 180; According to W.F. J. Jenner, *Memories of Luoyang, Yang Hsüan-chih and the lost capital (493-534)* (Oxford: Clarendon Press, 1981), the term *hu* in texts of the Six Dynasties period almost invariably refers to people of Western origin (generally from India and Indianized Central Asia) or to others with high noses and hairy faces, p. 86. The nomadic tribes on and around the borders of China who had interaction with Chinese culture were usually identified as Jie or Jie Hu and Rouran as well as other names.

10 J. Holmgren in her very interesting and insightful article, 'Northern Wei as a Conquest Dynasty: Current Perceptions; Past Scholarship,' *Papers on Far Eastern History* 40 (September 1989), pp. 1-3 discusses the various factors that have led to the neglect of Northern Wei history in the West. This neglect to some degree resulted from traditional Chinese approaches to Wei as a conquest dynasty and as illegitimate, an attitude that alternated between benign indifference, silent embarrassment or hostility.

11 Alexander C. Soper's analysis of the importance of 'South Chinese Influence on the Buddhist Art of the Six Dynasties Period,' *Bulletin of the Museum of Far Eastern Antiquities* 32 (1960), pp. 50-56, provided extraordinary insights by connecting scraps of literary evidence and limited Buddhist finds from Sichuan. However, his article had a biased view of the nomads reflected in his sub-section titled, 'The Dark Ages in the North.' A number of historians have also acknowledged the blurred boundaries between the nomads and Chinese as the acculturation process progressed unevenly on all levels of society: Holcombe, 'The Xianbei', pp. 22-29; Mark Edward Lewis, *China Between Empires, The Northern and Southern Dynasties* (Cambridge, MA. and London, England: The Belknap Press of Harvard University Press, 2009), p. 168; Pearce, Spiro and Ebrey, *Culture*, Introduction, pp. 1-35.

12 Thomas J. Barfield. *The Perilous Frontier* (Cambridge, MA.: B. Blackwell, 1989).

13 David B. Honey, 'Sinification as Statecraft in Conquest Dynasties of China: Two Medieval Case Studies,' *Journal of Asian History* 30 2 (1996), p. 116.

14 See Mark Elliott, '*Hushuo*', pp. 181-182 and Susan Bush, 'Thunder Monsters, Auspicious Animals, and Floral Ornaments in Early Sixth-Century China,' *Ars Orientalis* X (1975), pp. 19-33; Lewis, *China Between Empires*, pp. 167-168.

15 The variations in iconography visible on the fifth century *pushou* ranging from palmettes to infant Buddhas and West Asian deities require an extensive study which I am pursuing in the near future. A very similar mask with palmette tree was found in late fifth century Tomb No. 1, at Hudong in Datong. This is one of the larger tombs found since the discovery of the tomb of Sima Jinlong 司马金龙, Shanxi sheng Datong shi kaogu yanjiu suo 山西大同市考古研究所 [Archaeological Institute of Datong City, Shanxi] 'Hudong Bei Wei yihaomu' 大同湖东北魏一号墓 [No. 1 Northern Wei Tomb at Hudong, Datong], *Wenwu* 文物 12 (2004), pp. 26-34; p. 29: fig. 5. In recent years over three hundred Northern Wei tombs have been excavated east and south of Datong city. It has been suggested that this female deity on top of the single large *pushou* in the Kurland Collection may be a representation of the Goddess Nana whose animal attribute was a lion and who usually holds the sun and moon, one in each hand.

16 Annette L. Juliano and Judith A. Lerner, *Monks and Merchants, Silk Road Treasures from Northwest China, Gansu and Ningxia, 4th - 7th Century* (New York: Harry N. Abrams, Inc. with the Asia Society, 2001), *pushou* excavated from Leizumiao Village in Guyuan, Ningxia, pp. 83-84, figs. 17a, b; 18 a, b; Annette L. Juliano, *Unearthed, Recent Archaeological Finds from Northern China* (Williamstown, MA: Sterling and Francine Clark Art Museum distributed by Yale University Press, 2012), Song Shaozu's stone sarcophagus, Datong, pp. 43-46, with exterior covered with carved *pushou*; and recently a pair of gilt bronze *pushou*, each with figure holding the neck of dragons, see Chen Yongzhi 陈永志, Song Guodong 宋国栋, and Ma Yan 马艳, 'The Results of the Excavation of the Yihe-Nur Cemetery in Zhenxiangbai Banner (2012-2014),' *The Silk Road* 14 (2016), p. 47 (Pair of *pushou* from tomb M1).

17 Wu Hung, 'Buddhist Elements in Early Chinese Art (2nd to 3rd. C. A.D.)' *Artibus Asiae* Vol. XLVI, 3/4 (1986), pp. 269-270, figs.

11, 12. Wu saw this motif as deriving from a Chinese myth of 'Huan Long Shi,' the dragon tamer. The association was made after the motif was adapted into the Chinese vocabulary. James C.Y. Watt has suggested a link to the gold pendant ca. 1st c. BCE inlaid with garnet, lapis lazuli and turquoise at Tillye-Tepe, Northern Afghanistan, National Museum of Afghanistan, Kabul with antecedents farther West and as a motif possibly surviving from an earlier period of the Xianbei culture on the steppes, James C.Y. Watt, *Dawn of a Golden Age, 200-750 AD* (New York: Metropolitan Museum of Art and New Haven and London: Yale University Press, 2004), pp. 9-10, fig. 7; p. 164, no. 73 referring to an Inner Mongolian antecedent in no. 35 which is possibly connected to Bactria. Also see Juliano and Lerner, *Monks and Merchants*, pp. 83-84, figs. a, b and 18 a, b.

[18] Juliano, *Unearthed*, pp. 35-53; for the excavation report Shanxi sheng kaogu yenjiu suo 山西省考古研究所 [Shanxi Provincial Archaeology Institute] and Datong shi kaogu yanjiu suo 大同市考古研究所 [Datong City Archaeological Research Institute] 'Datong shi Bei Wei Song Shaozu *mu fajue baogao*' 大同市北魏宋绍祖墓发掘简报 [Brief Report of Song Shaozu's Northern Wei tomb, Datong City], *Wenwu* 文物. 7 (2001), pp. 19-39.

[19] Juliano and Lerner, *Monks and Merchants*, p. 79, fig. D, rubbing of the ornament from the two small stone bases from the tomb of Sima Jinlong (d. 484).

[20] Three-legged bronze basin with birds similar to those positioned on the outer edge of the large Kurland *pushou*, see Chen, Song, and Ma, 'The Results of the Excavation of the Yihe-Nur Cemetery,' p. 52, fig. 32.

[21] Both Jessica Rawson and Suzanne Valenstein have discussed this critical connection in their study of Northern Dynasties flamboyant appliqué ceramics, see Jessica Rawson, 'Central Asian Silver and Its Influence on Chinese Ceramics,' *Bulletin of the Asia Institute*, 5 (1991): pp. 139-151 and Suzanne G. Valenstein, *Cultural Convergence in the Northern Qi Period: A Flamboyant Chinese Ceramic Container, A Research Monograph* (New York: The Metropolitan Museum of Art, Asian Art Department, 2007), pp. 63-71.

[22] Archaeological evidence of iron stirrups found in Liaoning and then in Inner Mongolia. The stirrups provided a firm seat in the saddle for combat and shooting, coupled with the completely armored horse, creating a truly formidable Xianbei cavalry force. Holcombe, 'The Xianbei', pp. 21-22. Stirrups in tomb of Feng Sufu (d. 415) Beipiao, Liaoning, see Li Yaobo 黎瑶渤, 'Liaoning Beipiao sheng guan yingzi Bei Yan Feng Sufu mu' 辽宁北票县官营子北燕冯素弗墓 [Northern Yan tomb of Feng Sufu discovered at Beipiao officials camp in Liaoning] *Wenwu* 文物 3 (1973), pp. 2-28; fig. 43 (stirrups); iron stirrups also published by Watt, *Dawn*, p. 130, no. 41.

[23] Holcombe, 'The Xianbei', pp. 20, 23.

[24] Ibid., pp. 19-20; Lewis, *China Between Empires*, p. 114. Mark Lewis also points out that virtually all the non-Chinese dynasties, with few exceptions, forcibly resettled thousands of people around their capitals to engage in animal husbandry and agriculture to provide for the state and its armies, p. 138.

[25] Soper, 'South Chinese Influence', p. 53.

[26] Annette L. Juliano. *Buddhist Sculpture from China, Selections from the Xi'an Beilin Museum Fifth Through Ninth Centuries* (New York: China Institute Gallery, 2007), p. 4.

[27] Elliott, '*Hushuo*', p. 181.

[28] Soper, 'South Chinese Influence', p. 56. Holcombe, 'The Xianbei', p. 24.

[29] See description of the development of the city plan and the architecture by Nancy Shatzman Steinhardt, *Chinese Architecture in an Age of Turmoil, 200-600* (Honolulu: University of Hawai'i Press and Hong Kong University Press, 2014), p. 35.

[30] Soper, 'South Chinese Influence,' p. 51.

[31] Five Yungang colossi dedicated to the former Emperor and ancestors. Alexander C. Soper, 'Imperial Cave-Chapels of the Northern Dynasties: Donor, Beneficiaries, Dates,' *Artibus Asiae* Vol. XXVII, 4 (1966), pp. 242-243. The *Nan Qi Shi's* description of the capital of Pingcheng indicates that outside the Southern Gate were five temples corresponding to the five generations, see Lou Lin, 'A Study of the Civilization of the Northern Wei,' p. 97.

[32] Soper, 'Beneficiaries, Dates,' pp. 241-246.

[33] Los Angeles County Museum of Art, Overseas Archaeological Exhibition Corporation, The People's Republic of China, *The Quest for Eternity* (San Francisco: Chronicle Books, 1987), nos. 47-49 (Sima Jinlong).

[34] For an excellent discussion of the acculturation process between the nomads and the Chinese, see David B. Honey, 'Stripping off Felt and Fur: An Essay on Nomadic Sinification,' *Paper on Inner Asia* 21 (1992), pp. 1-39. The continuity of Chinese history owes a great debt to those dynasties founded and ruled by foreign houses. Honey's essay is intent on counterbalancing the traditional sinocentric biases of historical interpretation regarding nomads or barbarians, 'which downplayed the influence of periodic infusions of foreign blood.' (p. 3).

[35] Although many Chinese had fled south to escape from the Xianbei, others adopted Xianbei names and clothing and chose military careers rather than relying on connections to secure civil positions. Elliott, '*Hushuo*' pp. 180-182.

[36] Holcombe, 'The Xianbei', p. 14; Lewis, *China Between Empires*, p. 81.

[37] For descriptions of gardens tucked into private residences, temples, and monasteries see W.F.J. Jenner, *Memories of Loyang*, pp. 173; 241-244 and Yang Hsüan-chih, *A Record of Buddhist Monasteries in Lo-yang*, translated by Yi-t'ung Wang (Princeton, New Jersey: Princeton University Press, 1984), pp. 58-59; 191-196.

[38] Jenner, *Memories*, p. 104.

[39] Lewis, *China Between Empires*, p. 115.

[40] Jenner, *Memories*, p. 56.

[41] Ibid., p. 12.

[42] Albert E. Dien, *Six Dynasties Civilization* (New Haven and London: Yale University Press, 2007), p. 315; and Annette L. Juliano, 'Buddhist Sculpture: Innovation, Invention, and Imagination,' in *Art in a Time of Chaos, Masterworks from Six Dynasties China 3rd - 6th Centuries*, Willow Weilan Hai, Annette L. Juliano, Gong Liang, Shi Jnming, and Bai Ning (New York: China Institute Gallery, 2016), p. 104.

[43] Juliano and Lerner, *Monks and Merchants*, p. 136.

44 As Northern Wei began to wane in the 520s, a second limestone cave temple complex was opened east of Luoyang. Gongxian was less ambitious but still impressive, particularly Cave I, the largest. This cave supported by wealthy and influential donors had a beautifully coffered ceiling with lotus births and *apsaras* and imperial processions. The Kurland Collection has a small relief probably depicting attendants originally part of the imperial processions (cat. no. 21). Although displaying the iconic characteristics of the linear Northern Wei style, the figural style shows a bit more solidity.

See Henan sheng wenwuju gongzuo dui 河南省文物局文物工作队 *Gongxian shiku* 巩县石窟 *[Gongxian Cave Temples]* (Beijing: Wenwu chubanshe, 1963), Cave I, pls. 8-57, magnificent palmettes in the pointed arch above the Buddha's niche.

45 Soper, 'South Chinese Influence,' pp. 47-112. A somewhat different perspective is briefly articulated by Angela Falco Howard, 'From the Han to the Southern Song,' in *Chinese Sculpture*, by Angela Falco Howard, Li Sung, Wu Hung, and Yang Hong, *Chinese Sculpture* (New Haven and London: Yale University Press and Beijing: Foreign Languages Press, 1995), p. 236.

46 Horses had acquired an important position in Chinese culture. Henry Serruys, C.I.C.M, 'A Note on China's Northern Frontier,' *Monumenta Serica*. 28 (1969), p. 451 points out that in the Three Kingdoms period, the nomads, well aware of the Chinese need for horses, decided to sell no more horses in order to extract more concessions – to the great annoyance of the Chinese officials.

47 Juliano, *Unearthed*, pp. 105-6, figs. 2-3, some of the late fifth century clay tomb sculpture from Song Shaozu's (d. 477) tomb excavated near Datong and some from a set of five tombs excavated at Yanbei Teachers College, Datong, see Watt, *Dawn*, pp. 142-143, nos. 51, 52 and Sima Jinlong's tomb d. 484, excavated at Datong, p. 161, fig. 70. Luoyang Bowuguan, 洛阳博物馆 [Luoyang Museum], 'Luoyang Bei Wei Yuan Shao mu,' 洛阳北魏元邵墓 [Northern Wei Tomb of Yuan Shao at Luoyang], *Kaogu* 考古, 4 (1973), pp. 218-224, 243 and pls. 8-12; the change from the style of the Datong clay tomb sculpture can readily be seen by comparing the early sixth century examples from the tomb of Yuan Shao, Luoyang to those late fifth century figures from Sima Jinlong's tomb, Datong.

48 Lewis, *China Between Empires*, p. 83; Holcombe, 'The Xianbei', p. 30.

49 There are many publications dealing with the Qingzhou finds, perhaps the most accessible is the *Return of the Buddha, The Qingzhou Discoveries* (London: Royal Academy of the Arts, 2002), pl. 8-10.

50 Wang Huaqing ed., 王华庆, *Qingzhou Longxingsi fojiao zaoxiang yishu* 青州龙兴寺佛教造像艺术 [Buddhist Imagery at Longxing Temple of Qingzhou] (Shandong: Shandong chubanshe, 1999), pp. 30-40, pls. 33-44. *Return of the Buddha*, pp. 70-93, pls. 3-6, 8-9.

51 Juliano and Lerner, *Monks and Merchants*, p. 187, no. 66 and for the reference to Ajanta, Benoy K. Behl. *The Ajanta Caves: Ancient Paintings of Buddhist India* (New York: Thames & Hudson Inc., 1998), p. 66.

52 Xinru Liu. *Ancient India and Ancient China, Trade and Religious Exchanges AD1-600* (New Delhi: Oxford University Press, 1988), pp. 54-57.

53 See Tianshui Maijishan shiku yishu yanjiusuo bian, 天水麦积

山石窟艺术研究所编 [Edited by the Art Institute of the Maijishan Grottoes, Tianshui], *Zhongguo shiku Tianshui Maijishan* 中国石窟天水麦积山 [The Grotto Art of China, The Maijishan Grottoes, Tianshui], (Beijing: Wenwu chubanshe, 1998), Northern Wei Cave 142, for representation of coral in the chains of beads depicted on the seated Maitreya image. There are a number of examples of late Northern Wei and Eastern Wei bodhisattvas from the Qingzhcu finds with branching coral in the strings of jewelry. See *Return of the Buddha*, p. 90, fig. 9; p. 94, fig. 10; p. 100, fig. 12.

54 Juliano, *Beilin*, p. 7; Juliano and Lerner, *Monks and Merchants*, pp. 221-227.

55 Lewis, *China Between Empires*, pp. 116-117.

56 Juliano, *Unearthed*, ox painted on the ceiling of Luo Rui's tomb, p. 61, fig. 42. Excellent monograph provides an extensive detailed descriptions of the tomb contents and paintings illustrated with superb color photographs. Shanxi sheng kaogu yanjiu suo 山西省考古研究所 [Shanxi Provincial Institute of Archaeology] Taiyuan shi wenwu kaogu yanjiu suo 太原市文物考古研究所 [Taiyuan Municipal Institute of Cultural Relics and Archaeology] *Bei Qi Dong'an Wang Lou Rui Mu* 北齐东安王娄睿墓 [Lou Rui's Tomb] (Beijing: Wenwu chubanshe, 2006).

57 I-tien Hsing, 'Heracles in the East: The Diffusion and Transformation of his Image in the Arts of Central Asia, India, and Medieval China,' translated by William G. Crowell, *Asia Major*, Third Series, 28.2 (2005), pp. 103-154.

58 See three volumes edited by Wu Hung 巫鸿, *Han Tang zhi jian de zongjiao yishu yu kaogu* 汉唐之间的宗教艺术与考古 [*Between Han and Tang: Religious Art and Archaeology in a Transformative Period*] (Beijing: Wenwu chubanshe, 2000); *Han Tang zhijian wenhua yishu de hudong yu jiaorong* 汉唐之间的文化艺术的互动与交融 [Between *Han and Tang : Cultural and Artistic Interaction in a Transformative Period*] (Beijing: Wenwu chubanshe, 2001); *Han Tang zhi jian de shijue wenhua yu wuzhi wenhua* 汉唐之间的视觉文化与物质文化 [*Between Han and Tang: Visual and Material Culture in a Transformative Period*] (Beijing: Wenwu chubanshe, 2003).

A cogent overview of the origins of early medieval China studies is provided by a series of articles in 'The Birth of Early-Medieval China Studies,' special issue, *Asia Major*, 3rd series 23, no. 1 (2010).

# Bibliography

Barfield, Thomas J. *The Perilous Frontier*. Cambridge, MA.: Blackwell, 1989.

Behl, Benoy K. *The Ajanta Caves: Ancient Paintings of Buddhist India*. New York: Thames & Hudson Inc., 1998.

Bush, Susan. 'Thunder Monsters, Auspicious Animals, and Floral Ornaments in Early Sixth-Century China,' *Ars Orientalis X* (1975), pp. 19-33.

Chen Yongzhi 陈永志, Song Guodong 宋国栋, and Ma Yan 马艳, 'The Results of the Excavation of the Yihe-Nur Cemetery in Zhenxiangbai Banner (2012-2014),' *The Silk Road*, 14 (2016), pp. 42-57, pls. IV-VI.

Dien, Albert E. *Six Dynasties Civilization*. New Haven and London: Yale University Press, 2007.

Elliott, Mark. '*Hushuo*, The Northern Other and the Naming of the Han Chinese,' in *Critical Han Studies, The History and Representation and Identity of China's Majority*, edited by Thomas S. Mullaney, James Leibold, Stephane Gros, and Eric Vanden Bussche. Berkeley, Los Angeles, and London: University of California Press, 2012, pp. 173-190.

Gropp, Gerd. *Archäeologische Funde aus Khotan Chinesische-Ostturkestan: Die Trinkler-Sammlung im Übersee-Museum, Bremen*. Bremen: Verlag Friedrich Rover, 1974.

Henan sheng wenwuju wenwu gongzuo dui 河南省文物局文物工作队 *Gongxian shiku* 巩县石窟 [*Gongxian Cave Temples*], Beijing: Wenwu chubanshe, 1963.

Holcombe, Charles. 'The Xianbei in Chinese History,' *Early Medieval China* 19 (2013), pp. 1-38.

Honey, David B. 'Sinification as Statecraft in Conquest Dynasties of China: Two Medieval Case Studies,' *Journal of Asian History* 30.2 (1996), pp. 116-151.

Howard, Angela Falco, Li Sung, Wu Hung, and Yang Hong. *Chinese Sculpture*. New Haven and London: Yale University Press and Beijing: Foreign Languages Press, 1995.

Hsing, I-tien, 'Heracles in the East: The Diffusion and Transformation of his Image in the Arts of Central Asia, India, and Medieval China,' translated by William G. Crowell, *Asia Major*, Third Series, 28.2 (2005), pp. 103-154.

Jenner, W.F.J. *Memories of Luoyang, Yang Hsüan-chih and the lost capital (493-534)*.Oxford: Clarendon Press, 1981.

Juliano, Annette L. *Buddhist Sculpture from China, Selections from the Xi'an Beilin Museum Fifth Through Ninth Centuries*. New York: China Institute Gallery, 2007.

Juliano, Annette L. 'Buddhist Sculpture: Innovation, Invention, and Imagination,' in *Art in a Time of Chaos, Masterworks from Six Dynasties China 3rd - 6th Centuries*, Willow Weilan Hai, Annette L. Juliano, Gong Liang, Shi Jinming, and Bai Ning, New York: China Institute Gallery, 2016, pp. 101-116.

Juliano, Annette L. *Unearthed, Recent Archaeological Finds from Northern China*. Williamstown, MA: Sterling and Francine Clark Art Museum distributed by Yale University Press, 2012.

Juliano, Annette L. and Judith A. Lerner, *Monks and Merchants, Silk Road Treasures from Northwest China, Gansu and Ningxia, 4th-7th Century*. New York: Harry N. Abrams, Inc. with the Asia Society, 2001.

Lewis, Mark Edward. *China Between Empires The Northern and Southern Dynasties*. Cambridge, MA. and London, England: The Belknap Press of Harvard University Press, 2009.

Li Yaobo 黎瑶渤, 'Liaoning Beipiao sheng guan yingzi Bei Yan Feng Sufu mu' 辽宁北票县官营子北燕冯素弗墓 [Northern Yan tomb of Feng Sufu discovered at Beipiao officials camp in Liaoning] *Wenwu* 文物 3 (1973), pp. 2-28.

Liu, Xinru. *Ancient India and Ancient China, Trade and Religious Exchanges AD1-600*. New Delhi: Oxford University Press, 1988.

Los Angeles County Museum of Art, Overseas Archaelogical Exhibition Corporation, The People's Republic of China, *The Quest for Eternity*. San Francisco: Chronicle Books, 1987.

Lou Lin, 'A Study of the Civilization of the Northern Wei Dynasty in its Founding Period,' *Eurasian Studies*, English Edition IV, editors-in-chief, Yu Taishan & Lin Jinxiu, Asia Publishing Nexus, 2016, pp. 95-157.

Luoyang Bowuguan, 洛阳博物馆 [Luoyang Museum], 'Luoyang Bei Wei Yuan Shao mu,' 洛阳北魏元邵墓 [Northern Wei Tomb of Yuan Shao at Luoyang], *Kaogu* 考古, 4 (1973), pp. 218-224, 243 and pls. 8-12.

Ningxia Huizu zizhiqu Guyuan Bowuguan and Zhong Ri Yuanzhou lianhe kaogu dui 宁夏回族自治区 古原博物馆，中日原州联合考古队 [Guyuan Museum, Ningxia Hui Autonomous Region and China-Japan Yuanzhou Joint Archaeological Team], *Yuanzhou gumu jicheng* 原州古墓集成 [*Survey of Ancient Tombs of Yuanzhou*]. Beijing: Wenwu chubanshe, 1999.

Pearce, Scott, Audrey Spiro, and Patricia Ebrey, editors. *Culture and Power in the Reconstitution of the Chinese Realm*. Cambridge, MA. and London: Harvard University Asia Center and distributed by Harvard University Press, 2001.

Rawson, Jessica. 'Central Asian Silver and Its Influence on Chinese Ceramics,' *Bulletin of the Asia Institute*, 5 (1991), pp. 139-151.

Rudolph, Richard C. *Han Tombs Art of West China, A Collection of First and Second-Century Reliefs*. Berkeley and Los Angeles: University of California Press, 1951.

Serruys, Henry, C.I.C.M, 'A Note on China's Northern Frontier,' *Monumenta Serica*. 28 (1969), pp. 442-461.

Shanxi sheng Datong shi bowuguan 山西省大同市博物馆 [Datong City Museum, Shanxi Province] and Shanxi sheng wenwu gongzuo wei yuan hui 山西省文物工作委员会 [Shanxi Province Committee for Cultural Properties Work Team], 'Shanxi Datong Shijiazhai Bei Wei Sima Jinlong mu,' 山西大同石家寨北魏司马金龙墓, [Northern Wei Tomb of Sima Jinlong in Shi jiazhai, Datong, Shanxi,], *Wenwu* 文物 3 (1972), pp. 20-33, 64.

Shanxi sheng Datong shi kaogu yanjiu suo 山西大同市考古研究所 [Archaeological Institute of Datong City, Shanxi], 'Datong Hudong Bei Wei yi haomu' 大同湖东北魏 一号墓 [No. 1 Northern Wei Tomb at Hudong, Datong] *Wenwu* 文物12 (2004), pp. 26-34

Shanxi sheng kaogu yanjiu suo 山西省考古研究所 [Shanxi Provincial Institute of Archaeology] Taiyuan shi wenwu kaogu yanjiu suo 太原市文物考古研究所 [Taiyuan Municipal Institute of Cultural Relics and Archaeology] *Bei Qi Dong'an Wang Lou Rui Mu* 北齐东安王娄睿墓 [*Lou Rui's Tomb*], Beijing: Wenwu chubanshe, 2006.

Shanxi sheng kaogu yanjiu suo 山西省考古研究所 [Shanxi Provincial Archaeology Institute] and Datong shi kaogu yanjiu suo 大同市考古研究所 [Datong City Archaeological Research Institute], 'Datong shi Bei Wei Song Shaozu mu fajue baogao' 大同市北魏宋绍祖墓发掘简报 [Brief Report of Song Shaozu's Northern Wei tomb, Datong City], *Wenwu* 文物, 7 (2001), pp. 19-39.

Soper, Alexander C. 'Imperial Cave-Chapels of the Northern Dynasties: Donor, Beneficiaries, Dates,' *Artibus Asiae*, Vol. XXVII, 4 (1966), pp. 241-270.

Soper, Alexander C. 'South Chinese Influence on the Buddhist Art of the Six Dynasties Period,' *Bulletin of the Museum of Far Eastern Antiquities 32* (1960), pp. 47-107.

Steinhardt, Nancy Shatzman. *Chinese Architecture in an Age of Turmoil, 200-600*. Honolulu: University of Hawai'i Press and Hong Kong University Press, 2014.

Tianshui Maijishan shiku yishu yanjiusuo bian, 天水麦积山石窟艺术研究所编 [Edited by the Art Institute of the Maijishan Grottoes, Tianshui], *Zhongguo shiku Tianshui Maijishan* 中国石窟天水麦积山 [*The Grotto Art of China, The Maijishan Grottoes, Tianshui*], Beijing: Wenwu chubanshe, 1998.

Valenstein, Suzanne G. *Cultural Convergence in the Northern Qi Period: A Flamboyant Chinese Ceramic Container, A Research Monograph*. New York: The Metropolitan Museum of Art, Asian Art Department, 2007.

Wang Huaqing ed., 王华庆, *Qingzhou Longxingsi fojiao zaoxiang yishu* 青州龙兴寺佛教造像艺术 [*Buddhist Imagery at Longxing Temple of Qingzhou*], Shandong: Shandong chubanshe, 1999.

Watt, James C.Y. *Dawn of a Golden Age, 200-750 AD*. New York: Metropolitan Museum of Art and New Haven and London: Yale University Press, 2004.

Wu Hung, 'Buddhist Elements in Early Chinese Art (2nd to 3rd. C. A.D.)' *Artibus Asiae*, Vol. XLVI, 3/4 (1986), pp. 263-303; 305-352.

Wu Hung 巫鸿, *Han Tang zhi jian de zongjiao yishu yu kaogu* 汉唐之间的宗教艺术与考古 [*Between Han and Tang: Religious Art and Archaeology in a Transformative Period*], Beijing: Wenwu chubanshe, 2000; *Han Tang zhijian de wenhua yishu de hudong yu jiaorong* 汉唐之间的文化艺术的互动与交融 [*Between Han and Tang : Cultural and Artistic Interaction in a Transformative Period*], Beijing: Wenwu chubanshe, 2001; *Han Tang zhi jian de shijue wenhua yu wuzhi wenhua* 汉唐之间的视觉文化与物质文化 [*Between Han and Tang: Visual and Material Culture in a Transformative Period*], Beijing: Wenwu chubanshe, 2003.

Yang Hsüan-chih, *A Record of Buddhist Monasteries in Lo-yang*, translated by Yi-t'ung Wang, Princeton, New Jersey: Princeton University Press, 1984.

Zhonghua shiji tan yishu guan 中华世纪坛艺术馆 [China Millenium Monument Art Museum] and Qingzhou shi Bowuguan 青州市博物馆 [Qingzhou Municipal Art Museum], editors. *Qingzhou Beichao fojiao zaoxiang* 青州北朝佛教造像 [*Northern Dynasties Buddhist Images from Qingzhou*]. Beijing: Wenwu chubanshe, 2002.

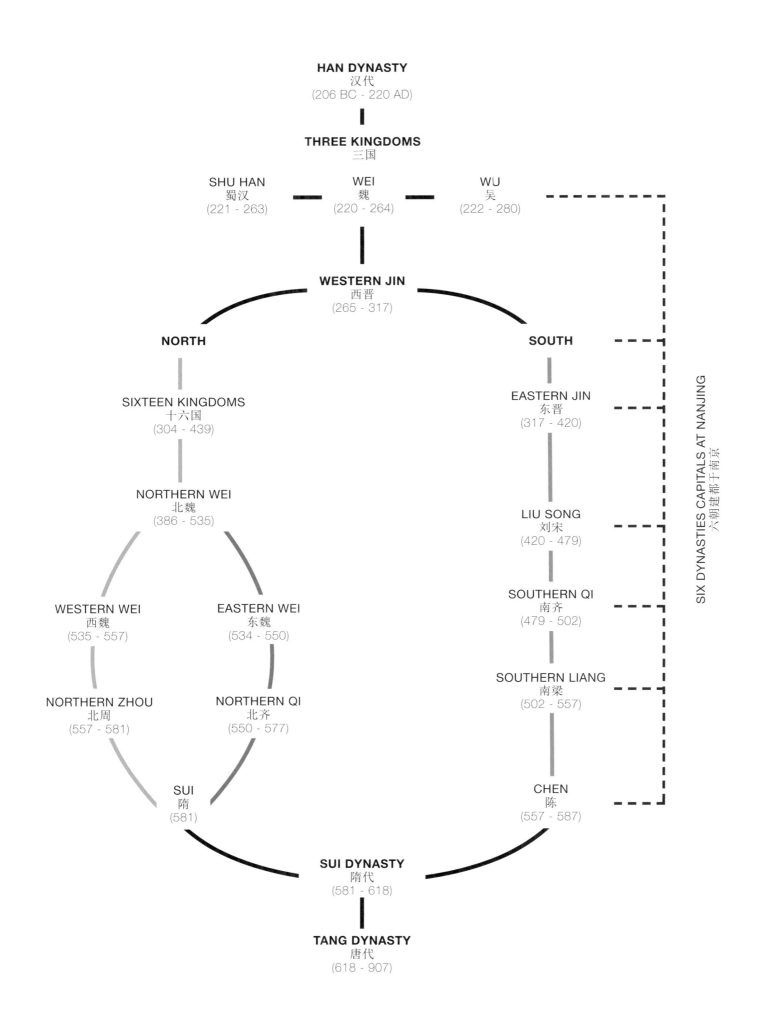

**HAN DYNASTY**
汉代
(206 BC - 220 AD)

**THREE KINGDOMS**
三国

SHU HAN
蜀汉
(221 - 263)

WEI
魏
(220 - 264)

WU
吴
(222 - 280)

**WESTERN JIN**
西晋
(265 - 317)

**NORTH**

**SOUTH**

SIXTEEN KINGDOMS
十六国
(304 - 439)

EASTERN JIN
东晋
(317 - 420)

NORTHERN WEI
北魏
(386 - 535)

LIU SONG
刘宋
(420 - 479)

WESTERN WEI
西魏
(535 - 557)

EASTERN WEI
东魏
(534 - 550)

SOUTHERN QI
南齐
(479 - 502)

NORTHERN ZHOU
北周
(557 - 581)

NORTHERN QI
北齐
(550 - 577)

SOUTHERN LIANG
南梁
(502 - 557)

SUI
隋
(581)

CHEN
陈
(557 - 587)

SIX DYNASTIES CAPITALS AT NANJING
六朝建都于南京

**SUI DYNASTY**
隋代
(581 - 618)

**TANG DYNASTY**
唐代
(618 - 907)

北朝 (386-581)：动荡时代的雕刻塑像
Annette L. Juliano

## 序幕

数十年来，Norman Kurland 一直是古代中国艺术的热诚敏锐收藏家。他主要聚焦从北朝以来，即三世纪晚期至六世纪晚期的墓葬文物与佛教雕塑，当时中国北方的命运正由来自东北和西北地区游牧民族所掌控着。作为一名真正的鉴藏家，他尽心理解更完整的北朝艺术与文化，进而激发其求学于伦敦大学亚非学院并获得双硕士学位外，也从科陶德艺术学院「佛教艺术：历史与修复」硕班课程中修业完毕。同时间，他亦努力不懈地琢磨他的抉择，缔造一个完善的优秀收藏。Kurland 对五世纪至六世纪晚期的佛教雕塑，以及自六世纪以降的非佛教陶制墓葬雕塑 (明器)，皆抱持热烈情感联系。就如同一只棱镜的多面体般，在他收藏中的文物反映了北朝艺术成就与视觉文化的一些基本面向。

## 乱世之史

在进行探索北朝艺术与文化之前，需要简述其构成基础的历史脉络。中国首要帝国汉代 (前206-220)，开创一个前所未有的繁荣时期。强大的军事力量使其扩展至西部边疆，并开启陆上贸易路线的早期阶段，也就是后来众所皆知的丝绸之路。然而，经过几世纪后，汉帝国遂为之崩溃。因为当时中国正卷入恶劣内战与游牧入袭，期间短暂成立的数个王朝，不论是由汉族或不同游牧民族所建立者，无不为了控制国土而展开斗争 (见三十四页)。最后汉代领域分裂为三国，而十六国则建立在北方和西北之地并短暂重叠，其中只有三个朝代是由汉人统治。三国并立的情况直至三世纪晚期，要到西晋 (265-317) 时才再次统一起来而维持五十二年之久，其试图重新光耀汉代的昔日辉煌，并复兴前朝旧都洛阳和长安 (今西安)。但是在317

年时，一支侵略游牧骑兵以锐不可挡的袭击攻势，重挫蹂躏了北方境地，留下两座尊荣帝都—洛阳与长安于阴霾废墟之中，此时西晋朝廷的残存者便逃往转进南方。就在克服已存在的南方精英世家抵制，以及逃难的北方流亡人士支持下，西晋遂更改国号为东晋 (317-420)，并在建康 (今南京) 设立新都与朝廷。另一方面直至四世纪晚期，在竞争激烈的游牧部落中，一支名为拓跋鲜卑的氏族联盟成功崛起，最终以北魏 (386-535) 旗号统一北方。[1]

## 北魏与拓跋鲜卑

在此时的分裂中国里，北方受到游牧民族统治，而南方则是由汉人管辖，开启了南北朝时代 (见三十四页、三十七页、地图A)。[2] 鲜卑族中的主要派系也就是拓跋氏，于386年在山西北部建立独立王朝称之北魏，并逐渐击败所有对手，且在398年时于平城 (今大同) 创设首都。[3] 当甘肃地区于439年被合并时，拓拔魏遂成功地一统北方之境。控制甘肃一地让北魏统治者，能够更易往来西部边疆。之后在493年至494年间，孝文帝把北魏首都从平城，其接近内蒙边境与鲜卑原乡，迁移至他重建的洛阳古城这座传统汉文化中心地。[4] 在新都之中，他的汉化政策规定汉语成为官方宫廷语言，并强求拓跋贵族采用汉人服饰和姓氏，并与汉族仕绅进行通婚。但到了六世纪初期，此项政策导致内部紧张局势，在统治朝廷和愤慨放弃拓跋遗产的反对部落贵族之间展开争执。一场场的权力斗争与嗜血杀戮，遂重返北方地区。至535年时北魏分裂为二，两者皆为鲜卑将官所创立 (地图B)。在西边，洛阳再次陷于灰烬劫难，强而有力的贵族世家和军武将官重新聚集长安，由将军宇文泰建立的西魏 (535-557) 共维持二十余年，之后宇氏族人发起宫廷政变而创设北周 (557-581) (地图B、C)。在东边，高欢建立的东魏 (534-550) 也维

持二十多年左右，并置新都于河北南方的邺城，之后高氏成员引发政变再次推翻王朝而成立北齐 (550-577) (地图 B、C)。因为北周和北齐皆试图并占对方领土且欲一统江山，造成不论是南北方或东西边，政治冲突总不断地发生。然而，在北周朝廷里的一位知名权臣和将军—杨坚，于581年登基为王成为文帝，终于统一南北建立隋代 (589-618)。最后中国在唐代 (618-907) 重建之下，再次见证恢弘帝国盛况，进而持续近三百年。

北朝的理解认知

汉代于220年的崩溃违背了「中国历史最坚持的理想」，也就是一统中国的概念。[5] 随后的中国历史学者便视这些混乱、失序与血腥朝廷斗争为主要负评。[6] 南北朝的分裂不仅代表一种地理实况，也象徵一个「文明」与「野蛮」的区别鸿沟。[7] 当然，在南朝的文献记载如《南齐书》或《魏虏传》当中，都试图低估拓跋文明的水平程度。[8] 这是因为南朝宣称其具有合法性，而对该帝王朝廷抱有高度忠诚，并视自身为汉式生活的守护者。基于有限资料或错误讯息，《魏书》里有时甚至会出现矛盾的叙述文字，这类南朝文献因而定义此段时期为「五胡乱华」。这些贬抑性的描述不但夸大南方发达国度的文化优势，也强加北方原始胡人的刻板印象。[9]

最初，与此类似的偏见说法，仍形塑着二十世纪的学术领域。但是约在二十多年前，吾人对南北朝时期的理解认知，开始从中西方学者相当不屑一顾的态度中有所转变，而他们原本多沉浸于汉唐帝国的辉煌事迹。[10] 时常出现令人难以置信的考古发掘和在美国、欧洲与亚洲等地所举办各类大小展览的密集曝光，都加深世人的丝路迷恋。在这段期间内，人们越来越认识到通过商业传播文化的关键作用，进而产生更多丰裕的学术成果和浓厚兴趣。因此这不再是某些学者所认为的「黑暗时代」，而是一个充斥连续性和断裂感的历史时期，从中可见到持久的中国价值体系，在世事无常变化里挣扎抗衡，在社会快速迁动

中消弥边界。[11] 最后至今，南北朝时期被视为唐代帝国与后世王朝成就的根本基础，同时其自身也是中国文化史上充满生气与活力的崭新纪元。而考古活动持续出现的墓葬内容和佛教材料，更是丰富了我们对南北朝的认识。

即便在上述的简要描写中，其历史概况也能传达此一时期的复杂程度与游牧民族征服者的重要角色。其实，中国历史不仅能以朝代兴衰的线性编年，亦能以中原居民 (华人或汉族) 与其游牧邻族之际遇起伏视之。[12] 事实上，在悠久卓越的历史中，几乎三分之一曾统治中国的帝王朝廷者皆非汉人 (游牧民族或非华族裔)。[13] 在以下的文章里并非有意作为北朝艺术历史风格发展的传统综论，而是藉此机会重新回顾关于北朝文化的认知与特色，并针对 Kurland 展示藏品之陶瓷、明器和佛教雕塑，予以讨论其艺术成就的来龙去脉。

独特的北方文化

北朝前后三百余年来的工艺制作，特别是明器和佛教雕塑、陶瓷与存世绘画，在一定程度上都证明当时文化的丰富变异。这种多元性来自于与北方中原传统汉族文化的相遇接触，共有五种影响来源：拓跋鲜卑的成功入袭与统治地位、佛教与其他宗教的引入到来、从西方至中国贸易路线网络所带来的物品、理念和人民、北方中国的区域文化，以及与被认为是中国文化价值保存者之南朝的往来互动。这些影响都在艺术中反映出来而衍生成为一个谱系。在一端是同化的纹样母题，例如来自西亚和欧洲古典世界的丰富花卉图汇、叶饰设计与涡卷样式，以及来自佛教艺术的莲花图案。这些纹饰大部份取代或并存于常见的汉式卷云纹，以作为装饰的铺底和图汇。而在谱系的另一端则是集锦汇聚，即中外母题彼此并列如同在墓葬艺术中所见，创造一个具有互动区域性艺术风格的独特北方视觉文化。[14]

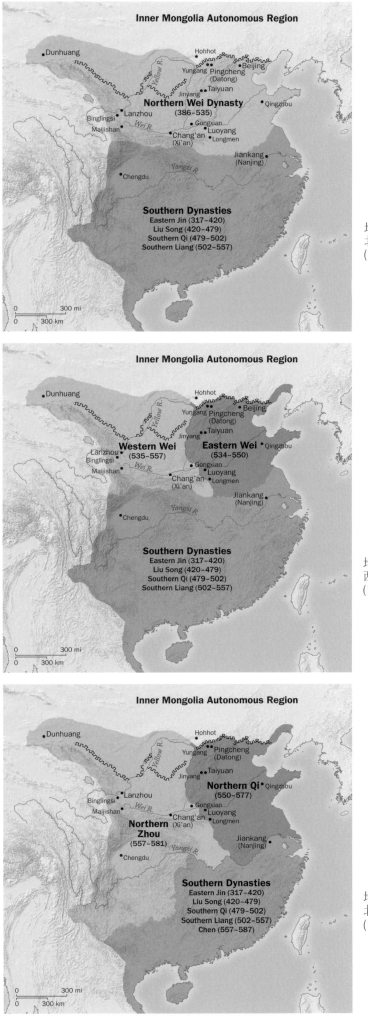

地图A
北魏与南朝疆域图
(Mapping Specialists, Ltd.)

地图B
西魏和东魏与南朝疆域图
(Mapping Specialists, Ltd.)

地图C
北周和北齐与南朝疆域图
(Mapping Specialists, Ltd.)

图1 a, b
两件东汉 (25-220) 墓门上的石刻铺首细部，现藏河南洛阳古墓博物馆。
a. 摄影：Annette L. Juliano
b. 摄影：Gary Lee Todd（维基共享资源：http://picasaweb.google.com/GaryLeeTodd 和 http://picasaweb.google.com/leefoxx1949/ 基于 GFDL 1.3 和 CC-by-SA-all 條款許可）

图2 a, b
五世纪晚期北魏鎏金铜铺首：
a. 面具上方的叶饰树样细部，Norman A. Kurland 收藏。(目录编号9)
b. 山西大同湖东北魏1号墓。(源自文物出版社，北京)

图3
面具上方的多臂人物细部，北魏青铜铺首，Norman A. Kurland 收藏。(目录编号8)

## 铺首、叶饰与其他域外纹样

Kurland 收藏中包括三件五世纪晚期的鎏金铜铺首，此为怪物或兽形面具，共有一对附衔环把柄的完整作品与一只遗失圆环的单独物件。另外还有两件北齐上釉陶瓷，一为青釉陶壶，另一则是绿釉圆罐。这些铺首与壶罐都展示出应用装饰纹样，代表传统中国工艺与上述非汉式纹样汇集的作用或对话（目录编号8、9、30、31）。通常来说，铺首是由一个具有凸眼的大型兽首、扩张鼻孔的三角直鼻、口中齿侧衔环以及从嘴里突出的一对利牙所组合而成，在其双眼之上可以有各类纹样图饰。这种带有环把的怪物或兽形饰物，有着悠久历史可远溯至西周青铜器皿。在战国时期，青铜铺首是被添置于木椁外部而作为象徵把柄。此类铺首亦雕刻于汉墓门口的石头上，在面具顶部展现三个三角状样式，也许是代表中央羽饰冠毛和一对触角或耳朵（图1a，b）。然而在北朝时代，特别是五世纪晚期的北魏，多数出自木椁的鎏金铜铺首，在纹样和图像上皆显示实质变化，如同 Kurland 藏品的三件铺首所精湛出示般（目录编号8、9）。就此对铺首来说，兽面上方充满着五瓣叶饰的中央羽饰冠毛，像极了一棵树木，并附加两只卷曲触角。而另一只较大的单件铺首，则有一尊四臂或六臂的女性神祇，正握持两个如狮首瘦长蛇身般的颈部（图2a和3）。[15] 具有叶饰或人物的相似铺首和相同的纹样母题配置，都可在五世纪晚期的北方境内见到，其遍布于宁夏固原、山西大同与内蒙等地（图5）。[16]

来自北方境内的许多铺首（包括衔环者）都有着人物形象，其正面握持汉式龙类或其他不太明确的兽种，其余则被装饰成植物纹样或卷曲触角。此种人物抓握迎面而来动物颈部的形象，可远溯至古代近东艺术。其象徵意涵为「万兽君王」而掌控动物世界，这个纹样图式可能是从大夏和犍陀罗地区流传至中国。[17] 在五世纪晚期大同宋绍祖墓的石棺四侧包括墓门与顶板，其表面即刻有铺首浮雕（图4a）。[18] 在这座石棺上，具有叶饰纹样的铺首、天人形象与缠绕于忍冬草纹里女伎人物等母题（图4b），皆可在司马金龙（卒于484年）墓室的石雕柱础与云冈石窟第10窟里被发

图4 a, b
a. 石刻铺首上方之握持兽角的女性人物，出土于宋绍祖墓石棺外侧，定年为477年，山西大同曹夫楼。（摄影：Annette L. Juliano）
b. 石刻柱座上之忍冬草纹与女伎人物拓片，石柱出土于琅琊王司马金龙（卒于484年）墓，山西大同。
（摄影：Annette L. Juliano）

图5
来自北魏墓葬（五世纪晚期）一对含有鎏金成份青铜铺首中的一只作品，出土于宁夏固原西郊螺祖庙。该握持兽颈的小型人物，有可能是描绘幼年佛陀。现藏固原博物馆，宁夏回族自治区。（源自宁夏文物考古研究所所长罗丰，宁夏回族自治区银川）

图6 a, b
a. 青釉陶人面纹壶，带有釉料模塑浮雕装饰，北齐（550-577），Norman A. Kurland 收藏。（目录编号31）
b. 带有蓄髭人面的模塑贴饰，于阗陶器，现藏国家冬宫博物馆，圣彼得堡。

现，两处都位于大同地区。[19] 另一个范例则出土于宁夏固原墓地，在面具上方及悬环上展现幼年佛陀形象（图5）。在此衔环的外圈之处，也附有类似猛禽的鸟类，而这些相近特徵都可在内蒙游牧民族的金属制品中寻找到。[20]

明显可见地，在 Kurland 收藏中来自北齐（550-577）的低温青釉陶壶，展现了一种迷人的集锦汇聚之感，也就是外观纹样印花分别应用至典型中国壶器表面之上，其包含珠状圆点中的中亚蓄髭人面、叶饰图案以及其他装饰贴花（目录编号31、图6a）。许多与这些纹样的明显相似处，可在约特干出土的陶器贴花中找到。该地是古代于阗王国的首都，位于新疆塔克拉玛干沙漠的南侧边缘，年代约为一至三世纪左右（图6a, b）。[21] 另一件精美平衡的绿釉陶圆盖罐，则有七个椭圆形章型纹，每一部份都以珠状饰边圈围住乐手或舞者（目录编号30，图7）。此类珠状饰边的章型纹，逐渐成为横跨中亚的广泛装饰图样，最早在五世纪中期已可见于佛教雕塑，直至六世纪中期以降遂广受欢迎。

第一座北魏首都：平城

从东汉（25-220）之始，拓跋氏便已沿着中国北方边境，即黄河上游境内与内蒙之间居住，并从这个区域邻近处获得熟悉汉人民间与军事生活方式的特色。拓跋鲜卑的军队人员，特别是其强大有力的骑兵队伍，支持他们成功拓展至中原地区。直至439年，拓跋鲜卑军团已征服甘肃地区，北魏便获得整个北方的掌控权。[22] 在他们延伸至中国「核心地带」期间，拓跋领导者曾透过汉籍文士的协助来统治帝国，并寻求巩固其军事胜利，逐渐仰赖汉式的官僚行政管理。[23] 此举创造出外来异族与中土汉人之间相互依存的文化和社会，开启了同化适应的复杂过程。

在398年时，两个北魏首都中的第一座都城，是由拓跋珪于平城建立。其位于山西北端离内蒙边境数哩处，就在长城之内靠近鲜卑的故土原乡和放牧地

区。为了期冀一座伟大的首都城府，他下令迫置五十万人定居城内与周遭近处，其中包括来自东部与其他异族的善巧艺匠十万名。[24] 在征服甘肃之后，姑臧（今武威，也曾是北凉 [398-439] 首都）的居民人口被迫撤离城市，并从西部迁移到平城安置，带来更多才艺能人与本土和外国僧侣的佛教热诚。在《魏书》中曾记载「凉州平，徙其国人于京邑，沙门佛事皆俱东，象教弥增矣。」[25] 凭藉其位置优越，甘肃，坐落于进入中国的丝路之上，促进西方艺匠和教士的频繁接触，并鼓励异域范式的模仿活动以便为这个新兴的外来宗教—佛教而制作造像，并在中国传播远扬。[26] 拓跋氏之前就已热诚地奉行与赞助佛教，而要比汉人普遍更甚北方。[27]

图7
绿釉陶圆盖罐，带有七个章型纹，都具珠状边饰和中亚吹笛弹琴的乐手舞者之模塑浮雕，北齐 (550-577)，Norman A. Kurland 收藏。(目录编号30)

当拓跋珪构筑他第一个正式首都平城时，作为一座盛大的皇家都城，其立即启动重大建设工程，包括主要佛院、僧侣厅堂、五层楼塔、宫殿宗祠、祀典祭坛与太庙明堂等。约在430年至470年左右达至高峰，平城已成为真正的皇室聚居区，其宫殿、御园、池苑与宅邸，都仅限于拓跋氏与其官宦臣员，当中一些无疑是汉人。这座城市规划反映了拓拔统治者对于中国帝都基本特色的认知了解。与此同时，平城也是一座混合汇聚之都，在城郭外有着指定区域的毡房营帐，用来适应传统的游牧生活方式。平城是个活跃的贸易枢纽，与来自中亚、费尔干纳、喀什米尔、波斯与高句丽等地的商客使团往来。其同时也是佛教中心，约有百间佛教机构和两千余位僧尼居住于此。[28] 在今日大同底下的平城近期发掘当中，已证实《魏书》对平城所述之宏伟模样。[29] 这些都与南朝特使所传达的印象（如刘宋 [420-479] 之《宋书》）在某种程度上产生矛盾，因为他们只见到「对其来说不过是十足野蛮行为的浅薄汉化虚饰而已」。[30]

图8
结跏趺坐的释迦佛尼佛，云冈石窟第20窟，山西大同郊外，凿刻于砂岩壁之上，可定年至460年左右。
(摄影：Annette L. Juliano)

## 云冈和五世纪佛教雕塑

在平城之西10哩之处，存在着最著名的石窟寺院—云冈，其于五世纪中期对外开放。现存的佛教洞窟遗址与新出石室以及数百佛教造像埋藏处的持续研究

图9
菩萨头像，云冈石窟第18窟，山西大同郊外；宝冠显示来自西亚的图样，包括珠状边饰、叶饰、圆轮和月牙等。（摄影：Annette L. Juliano）

图10 a, b
a. 握举钵匣飞扬的砂岩天人像，从风格、雕塑和石材来看，极有可能源自云冈石窟，Norman A. Kurland 收藏。
b. 鲜卑陶制墓葬人物头像，出土于山西大同司马金龙（卒于484年）墓。该天人和鲜卑人的面貌特征极为相似。（源自文物出版社，北京）

和发掘，都无法减低云冈对五世纪佛教造像贡献的重要性。在砂岩石壁上开凿出来的首要五所皇家洞窟其编号为16至20，而两座较小但仍属壮观的成对石室其编号为7和8以及9和10，都大约完成在460年至470年左右。[31] 在这五所皇家洞窟的每一座中，都有一尊庞大朝南的中央佛像，几乎要填满浅状椭圆窟室。第20窟和第17窟则是其宏观简穆与雕塑风采里最引人注目者。来自甘肃的一位僧侣—昙曜，说服皇帝以支持此项造像计画，不仅替前朝皇帝偏执迫害佛教徒之举而忏赎罪过，也藉此作为北魏王权的象徵意涵。拓跋统治者对佛教的奉行与赞助，让此外来宗教能够向异族和汉人传布宣扬，有助统一帝国，并赋予北魏更大的合法性，进而融合政治与宗教权力。

第20窟的40尺坐佛和第18窟的51尺立像，传达出隆重纪念和广阔气势的感受氛围（图8）。两侧有着修长大耳和覆盖的柔软发丝与顶髻，他们脸上精锐凿刻且轮廓分明的相貌以及「古意微笑」的特徵，无不结合力量强度和宽宏大度。而其长袍衣饰、装饰边纹、叶蔓花饰和菩萨宝冠的配置，亦反映深刻的西方来源，大部份是来自中亚、秣菟罗和犍陀罗的雕刻因素（图8和9）。然而，这些形象却显示一种超越的综合状态，不仅仅只是复刻重制而已。正如 Alexander C. Soper 博士指出，因为没有准确的原型存在，也没有外籍匠师或僧侣主管的参与文献证明，因此「可能是透过小型便携造像、绘画或图像纹样书册，而把西方前例传递于此」—亦有可能经由行旅人士的模糊描述而加以补充。[32]

在 Kurland 所收集的佛教雕塑里，共有五件五世纪的作品，对于石刻或铜铸的早期造像制作上提供深刻洞察。这些文物不但在很大程度上取决于异域范式，也与云冈风格产生共鸣。两件属于砂岩的造像，一是天人，另一则是残余头部与肩膀的佛陀（图10a，目录编号4），都极有可能来自云冈，年代约为五世纪晚期以降，即480年至490年左右。通常雕刻在石窟上方或藻井之处的天人，多以透过飘扬巾带、提带供品和随侍神祇的方式而缓缓飞落。在此虽然没有披帛出现，但 Kurland 所藏的天人

正握举一件钵匣，里头可能装满水果；其简洁俐落的刻画手法，使人物传递一种柔和优雅气质。有趣的是，在整幅面孔中的一些细小特征，亦与鲜卑容貌彼此相似，一如从大同出土的司马金龙墓中陶制墓俑饰品般（图10b）。[33] 另外对于 Kurland 的佛头肩像藏品来说，似乎反映五世纪晚期的变化，可见于其头部比例和较为细长的外形，传递出更多的汉地特色。

坐于须弥山形宝座之上的三件青铜佛像，每一位主角的袈裟都以开放式的形制风格而成垂下褶状，即部份露出右肩并展现对角交叉胸前的内衬。在内衬边缘和零星袈裟上都有着珠状边饰，这是来自中亚普遍存在的纹样（目录编号2、3、图8、11、12、13）。此三件作品中的两尊佛像，展示出袈裟边缘正从左肩垂挂而下，造成重复折叠的弯曲形状。在这三件五世纪青铜造像上，所见到佛陀衣纹的一般配置和袈裟折叠的连续接合，皆呼应云冈最早开凿五窟的主要风格特色。在方形青铜坐台边缘处所出现的珠状饰边，则再次重复云冈中央大佛的纹样联系，同样设计亦见于其胁侍菩萨、顶篷龛檐、明显非汉族面容的天人以及印度图像细节如对角横跨的璎珞项圈等处（图13）。其中一件鎏金铜佛坐像，定年于太和年间的482年，即约五世纪晚期二十五年间，是此时期从河北和山西产出卓越鎏金铜像的极佳范例（目录编号2、图11）。在宝座上的植物和叶饰卷纹与莲瓣，都成为中国装饰图汇的主流纹样。

### 第二座北魏首都：洛阳

从471年至499年统治北魏的孝文帝，首先定都平城。在493年至494年间，他迁都河南洛阳，不仅复兴这座古都，也从平城带来五十万人口。孝文帝以推动和实施激进汉化政策而闻名于世。[34] 在迁移至洛阳后，孝文帝即在宫廷中采行汉语且禁用外语。并要求朝臣穿着汉服与使用汉名。这项政策改变并不一定是因为渴望成为汉人而引发的，而是透过中央集权与推动文化适应，尽量减少异族和汉人之间的冲突，让拓跋游牧

图11
鎏金铜佛坐像，定年为482年，可见到云冈风格的因素，且其叶饰卷纹和莲瓣，都已融入中国佛教和装饰图汇中，Norman A. Kurland 收藏。（目录编号2）

图12 a, b
a. 坐于须弥山形宝座之上的小型弥勒铜像；可见其袈裟和内衬达缘的珠状边饰，以及宝座周围的缠绕绳纹样式，Norman A. Kurland 收藏。（目录编号3）
b. 宝座周围的缠绕绳纹样式细部。

图13
坐于须弥山形宝座之上的佛陀青铜饰板，Norman A. Kurland 收藏。

民族统治能依循中国王朝模式而合法化，使之更加容易治理一个多民族的社会。[35] 在洛阳朝廷里的拓跋中坚份子，并非要成为汉人精英的「复制品」。这些政策支持一个崭新汇聚精锐群体的崛起，通过拓跋皇室和汉族的联姻互婚，进而融合汉式和鲜卑特色，并在朝廷中给予平等的仕宦地位和头衔。汉人一鲜卑的相互嫁娶是打造混合精英家族的决定因素，这也成为日后统一时隋唐社会的根本基石。[36] 然而，往南重新迁都洛阳和皇帝朝廷对于汉风导向的增强，都让部份拓拔氏派系加以抵制，而最终导致王朝的垮台陷落。

如同在平城的拓跋珪般，孝文帝也有雄心壮志的建设计画，想要继续在皇家领导下迅速重建这座古都皇城。洛阳并非是一个自然成形的都市，整座都城特色皆在皇帝的督导下设计规划，并为此费时二十年之久历经数代帝王才得以完工。在当时对洛阳的描述中指出，其宫殿、楼阁和寺院都曾有着壮丽场景。明显地，一些庭苑也是由皇室成员、富豪平民和佛教僧官所建造起来。杨衒之《洛阳伽蓝记》曾描述超过二十座的花园，其重现山川谷地、佛教极乐莲池与异国植物、水果、鸣禽和虫蝉。[37] 而在内郭城里仅限宫殿、官府和佛教建筑，其余都城部份则遵循孝文帝的计画而以网格区分围墙里坊。[38] 在东区主要是附有市场的住宅群，而北区留有大型开放空间以训练军伍。另一个大型住宅外国社群，有可能多达五万居民，则在南区被分离出来，也为外籍旅客和移民提供庇护。西区部份限于皇室成员及其亲属、寺院、市场、商贾和艺人所居。都城中最热络的经济活动，乃是来自外地奢侈品和异国物的进口贩售。[39]

刚从平城迁都之后，孝文帝（逝世后庙号高祖）下令在洛阳内城中，除了知名的木造永宁塔和尼院外，不准建立其他任何寺庙，但这项禁令在他过世后便有所变化。[40] 就在洛阳城几近完工不久，随后的统治者和精英群便将财富和精力转向寺院庙宇的建设工作之上。这股宗教热情渗透了整座都城，最终竟暴增出现超过千栋建筑物。此外还有许多节庆典礼和豪华游行，佛教人物造像遂在街上传布流转，与杂耍和伎乐群众一起庆祝佛诞与其他活动。[41]

图14
龙门石窟，位于河南洛阳郊外开凿在石灰岩壁上；宾阳窟中洞，其主尊佛像定年为523年；在衣摺层叠之上展现成熟的北魏风格，正面图与侧视图。
（摄影：Annette L. Juliano）

龙门石窟寺和六世纪早期佛教雕塑

为了纪念他的父亲，孝文帝曾赞助宾阳窟中洞的开凿，其位于洛阳南方7.5哩被称为龙门石窟的硬质石灰岩壁中。完成于523年，该窟与其佛陀、僧伽和菩萨的雕刻塑像，都以它们独特的北魏雕塑风格而著称，可定年为六世纪初期二十五年间。虽然这种风格已在五世纪后期出现，一如云冈第6窟所示，但直至宾阳窟出现时才达到高峰。这类崭新雕塑概念已不再强调身躯构成，即透过人物衣裙、服袍与披巾律动摆摺所造成的复杂图式之下予以弱化。此种服饰风格就是所谓的「褒衣博带」，其松散外袍宽袖可在前部敞开垂挂，且在腰部之上系绑结带显露内衬（图14）。[42] 这款衣服配置实际上是佛教袈裟的重新诠释，混合汉地和印度元素。[43] 随着布料的复杂层层堆叠，让重点关注从身躯上转离出来，而在佛像的头顶和双手间，形成一个关键的视觉三角焦点。

在 Kurland 收藏里的四件小型雕塑中，两件是石灰岩另两件为青铜，皆捕捉到这类高度独特风格的强烈线条感和引人注目的精神风采（目录编号 13、26、图15a，b）。尤其当中两件青铜造像，一是定年为539年的坐像与另一定年为516年的广布鎏金立像，都反映此种北魏风格的极致表现，其身躯被对称布置的层叠布料包覆起来，而在底部呈现更多棱角（图15a、b）。这尊鎏金铜菩萨立像有着裳裙和披巾，其在腿部两侧飘逸飞扬，并往外向上散发动感气势，直指火焰形的背光之处（图15b）。在六世纪初期二十五年间，此创新风格图汇正主导形塑洛阳地区的佛教造像和陶制墓葬雕塑。在这里所展示出来的精湛工艺，以及 Kurland 收藏中来自六世纪早期雅致卓越的陶制墓葬雕塑，都是反映此种塑像概念的最佳写照，强调佛教与非佛教艺术之间的风格交流。[44]

当时佛教雕塑特色中的这些剧烈变化，通常可归功于南朝精湛汉族匠师的影响，如同在四川成都发现的造像所示，其定年最早可至483年。这个说法是由 Soper 于1960年代首先提出，并在日后的五十多年间持续展开辩

图15 a, b
a. 铜佛坐像，具有纤细身躯和衣摺层叠为充分发展的北魏佛像风格，Norman A. Kurland 收藏。(目录编号26)。
b. 鎏金铜菩萨立像，由其铭文可定年为516年，具有典型北魏锐角的「鱼尾式」垂帛，Norman A. Kurland 收藏。(目录编号13)

图16
彩绘陶马，其「无主」形貌通常在丧礼过程中视为是表现亡者；北魏，六世纪初期二十五年间，Norman A. Kurland 收藏。(目录编号23)

图17 a, b
a. 陶制墓葬武士护卫俑，来自六世纪初期二十五年间，反映洛阳地区平面化的雅致风格，Norman A. Kurland 收藏。
b. 陶制墓葬上釉带盔武士俑，出土于司马金龙 (卒于484年) 墓。(源自文物出版社，北京)

论。[45] 然而，不论南方的强大刺激是否对北方的雕塑发展有所贡献，这股在北方兴起的潮流，正是一种汇聚各方影响力的综合成果，创造出一个独特的北方风格。

「洛阳」风格之六世纪早期陶制墓葬雕塑

Kurland 收藏的核心强项之一，即为陶制墓葬雕塑的绝佳范品，其定年为六世纪初期二十五年间，与上述讨论的佛教造像有着类似的风格特征。从至今的考古记录来看，已在洛阳地区发现大量可资比较的案例。但令人遗憾的是，除了唐代同类作品外，此种陶制墓葬雕塑一直在中国雕塑层级中，处于模棱两可的地位处境，多被认定是社会学或人类学的史料记录，而非承认其艺术美感效度。但来自 Kurland 收藏中的许多优美范例，则是挑战这种观点。在此处的武士和文官护卫俑，表现出细长扁平身躯，几乎是以二度平面的浅浮雕方式和细部的精致线条对称刻画展示；两者都有极致的高挑细瘦模样，创造极为优雅的人物形象。特别在武官部份，尤为强调正面感和对称性，其内省微笑的细小面容特徵，传达了严肃和尊严而几乎成为一种典型标志 (目录编号10)。在藏品中的十五件坐姿乐伎 (目录编号15) 和双胞俑 (目录编号11)，都有着神秘的一抹微笑；令人关注地，可能来自欧洲神话的持盾武者以及源于西方外族脸孔的异域人士，则都有高鼻、深目与蓄胡外观。而全部的模型作品，包括狗、牛、马和笨拙骆驼，其蹄脚站立并扬头高露出如长刀般的颈部，皆表达出这些独特雕塑特质的多样变化。在被称为是此种「洛阳风格」的名品里，一件神采洋溢且披覆华丽鞍垫的无主陶马，即象徵丧礼过程中的亡者。作为 Kurland 藏品中的杰出范例，此马具有显著紧绷成拱状的颈部，并逐渐缩小成为锐利如刀刃般的边缘，最后于狭长的头部之处结束 (目录编号23、图16)；其丰富马饰的多变纹理是以浅浮雕的手法制作，凸显优美样式的雅致氛围而不减少一丝活力感。[46]

通过比较大同五世纪晚期和洛阳六世纪初期的埋葬文物，此类陶制墓葬雕塑的概念转变可以很快地被掌握住（图17a，b）。[47] 如前所述，在佛教造像中这种风格变化的因素，始出现于480年至490年左右的云冈第6窟，而后在六世纪初期二十五年间的龙门极致发展，同样情况亦见于巩县的较小石窟寺以及小型便携铜铸与石刻造像。然而，在陶制墓俑方面，似乎在迁移新都至洛阳后，其明显变化就已发生，有可能是受到佛教样式的启发所致。

图18
具有三位天人的石灰岩背光残片，附含颜料和金箔痕迹，由其铭文可定年为536年，东魏(534-550)，Norman A. Kurland 收藏。

## 北魏衰亡陷落、鲜卑统治复兴与东魏佛教雕塑

北魏掌权者遭遇到卫成军队的叛乱，并引发整个北方的其他起义暴动，造成北部领土分裂为两个王朝。在西方，国祚甚短的朝代为西魏（535-557）和之后的北周(557-581)，而其在东方的对立者，则为东魏（534-550）和北齐(550-577)（参见地图B、C）。在东部的两个国度，都是由高氏家族掌控，代表军武王朝主义和重振鲜卑风俗和语言。[48] Kurland 主要致力收藏焦点在东魏和北齐佛教造像传统的丰富特性之上，并以几件择优的陶制墓葬雕塑作品相互配衬。当中有两件东魏佛教雕塑：一个残片与一尊庄严宝饰的立姿菩萨。残片作品保存了造像背光上方右侧区域，由其铭文可定年为536年（图18）。三位完整伎乐天人和第四位零星部份被保存下来，展示一种连续性以及从北魏到东魏风格和图像的初期变化。飞袭天人的巾带依然保留北魏衣摺的线性动感，然而它们却有着较为结实的雕塑身驱。

图19 a, b
a. 石灰岩菩萨立像，尽管遗失手足部份，但仍具青州出土文物的典型风格特徵，展现融入璎珞垂带的鲜明珠饰，东魏 (534-550)，Norman A. Kurland 收藏。(目录编号27）
b. 围绕观音菩萨颈部的相似珠饰，绘制于阿旃陀石窟第1窟室壁上，可定年至500年。(源自Open source: The Yorck Project, Indischer Maler des 7 Jahrhunderts-001.jpg)。

第二件东魏雕塑作品，亦与在山东青州所发现的数件雕塑类似，[49,50] 是一尊优美宝饰的立姿菩萨，但很可惜遗失手足部份（目录编号27、图19a、20a）。在这尊菩萨雕像上还可见到两个精彩特色，反映首都邺城和其他北方城市的国际氛围。首先是连串珠饰的厚实璎珞，其间布满章纹、吊坠和珠宝，并穿插零星珊瑚装饰。这些对角交叉的饰物结线，可令人想起其印度原型。并能

图20 a, b
a. 石灰岩菩萨立像，配饰融入分枝珊瑚的璎珞垂带，东魏 (534-550)，Norman A. Kurland 收藏 。 (目录编号27)
b. 在甘肃南方麦积山石窟第142窟的六世纪早期弥勒菩萨坐像中，也可发现类似附有珍贵珊瑚的璎珞垂带。 (源自文物出版社，北京)

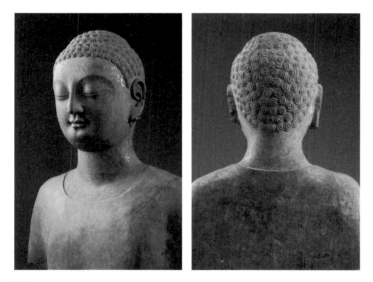

图21
砂岩佛头肩像，反映北齐 (550-577) 笈多风格的强烈影响。佛陀螺纹卷发细部，此为笈多风格的典型样式，Norman A. Kurland 收藏。

在定年为五至六世纪阿旃陀石窟第1窟里，所绘观音菩萨围绕其颈的串珠中，见到较为轻盈精致版本的宝饰 (图19b)。[51] 第二个显著特色则是分枝珊瑚饰品的刻画表现，在中国这被认为是奢华生活的象徵，而在印度笈多王朝时亦所费不赀。北朝期间的珊瑚极有可能是通过伊朗，从印度横经中亚之陆路而抵达中国 (图20a)。[52] 到目前为止，关于菩萨宝饰中珊瑚刻画的类似表现，已在北齐其他菩萨造像里发现到，亦见于甘肃南方麦积山石窟第142窟北魏菩萨的璎珞之上 (图20b)。[53]

以下讨论的东魏佛教造像和三件北齐佛像，都传达北朝时代佛教艺术的本质特徵，其整合透过陆路与海上来自西亚、东南亚和印度影响的持续潮流，以及来自邻近西魏和北周之北方境内与南朝等地的区域风格。尽管一些绿洲里中亚王国的动荡情势，时常打乱经由甘肃的陆路交通，但因土耳其人加强对中亚的控制，以致行经的外交使臣、商人贾客与传教僧侣，于六世纪中期又再度恢复他们的往来活动。北方城市如甘肃天水、陕西长安和宁夏固原等地，都见证该地区里异国贸易人士的逐渐汇聚成形。[54] 北齐首都邺城在异族人口居住上也有明显成长，大批的印度人与波斯人相继进入，且对外国货物的需求极为旺盛。当时南朝首都建康也是货物进出口和经销分售的主要港岸，因为商品和业者可以轻易地沿着区域河道系统而游移四方。

北齐佛像和印度笈多风格 (300-600)

北齐雕塑的佛教和非佛教造像，皆与北魏雕塑样式的线性化和无重感断除联系，其身躯已从堆叠衣饰的层级刻画中明显现露。在 Kurland 收藏里的三件佛像，反映印度笈多风格 (300-600) 强力影响的优异适应，该种艺思显然是与其他奢侈品在此时传入中国。这类作品的精湛造型，透过细薄的贴体袈裟而展露温和的圆躯样式，并以稀少的衣饰摺纹维持简易与整齐，传递出一股柔和感性 (目录编号29、37)。第三件佛像则显示典型的笈多元素，其巧工螺纹卷

发、细长莲瓣眼型、俯视沉思眼神以及感性双唇的敏锐塑造，形成一丝高深莫测的神情微笑。虽然只有头部与上胸存留下来，但此尊造像仍是北齐佛教雕塑中的极致作品，其不仅包覆一股奇特优雅气质，亦投射全然沉浸的灵性风采（图21）。笈多造像的影响力不但跨越中亚陆路，也可能透过海路方式，从建康的主要转运港而进入中国。除了明显的笈多美学外，北齐雕塑亦反映高度多样化的艺术环境，采行各类文化来源的图式样貌，并应用于不同媒材和脉络中，例如玻璃、金工、陶瓷以及墓葬壁画和殡葬石棺。[55]

北齐陶制墓葬雕塑

在 Kurland 收藏中的北齐墓葬雕塑，特别是披挂装饰的马匹和牛，透过色彩和贴花细节的加强，展现出活泼健壮的模样(目录编号34、38、图23c)。在犄角牛上头，仍保有细致的绘制双目，其上有卷翘眼睑而下方有睫毛留存（图22）。该特征和样式让头部与整体有着栩栩如生的感觉，这与山西太原南郊北齐娄睿墓顶北端的绘制牛，拥有共同的充沛活力样貌。[56] 横挂在牛背上的三条饰带，其结绳终端附有狮头与珠饰，而张口之处亦有流苏出现（图23a）。与此相同的图式可见于北齐的许多制作脉络里，包括 Kurland 所藏的陶制马匹臀部上与凶猛青铜狮兽面具中（图23b, c）；这种狮头类型可在墓葬守卫陶俑的盾牌中发现到，其头盔上亦经常显示狮子图像。这些头像样式可远溯至希腊神话人物赫拉克利斯身上；从地中海地区通过阿富汗和北印度，横跨中亚至西部而后中原，该图像学上的头部细节、狮身外观与棍棒造型，遂在各种变异当中辗转行旅。[57]

结语

如前所述，本篇文章并非有意要作为 Kurland 完整收藏之全面、历时、艺

术史或风格上的调查研究，而是透过在历史脉络中所精选出来的名品和群作，努力重塑关于北朝艺术成就的理解认知。即便在持续的动荡不安中，北朝时期的多元面向文化依旧蓬勃发展。在其艺术里清晰易见地的多样化和丰富度，实受到显著文化界限之流动性或「渗透力」的刺激，这与中土汉人和拓跋鲜卑之间文化适应的转变程度息息相关，亦涉及南朝与北方的互动往来。此时外来影响的集锦汇聚可谓实至名归，展示广泛的显露范围和接受能力，特别是佛教，其文物和仪式通过陆上丝路、草原地带和航运海线而抵达中国。这种强烈交叉孕育滋养了独特的北朝美学，最终吸收融入唐代帝国的艺术成就中。

当前这些新出考古发现的范围、数量和品质无不令人吃惊，例如山东青州佛教造像的精彩窖藏、长安出土定为571年并附有粟特文与汉文双语铭记的史君石椁、太原娄睿墓室墙壁上的华丽马画，以及各个精英墓葬里所埋藏的异域金工、珠宝和玻璃制品，都促使吾人进一步重新思量北朝对中国艺术和文化的贡献。新出考古资讯的不断涌现，加上学术研究的持续积累，已提升南北朝的地位至如实具有的变革性质。[58]

透过致力北朝的雕刻塑像，Norman Kurland 得以验证其个人热情和愿景；当他开始对北魏陶制墓葬雕塑展开收藏之旅时，此类文物还未受到关注，并远不及唐三彩墓葬雕塑的普及广泛。作为一位收藏名家，他的精选藏品为我们提供一扇着实令人启发的窗口，能够见识到藏家成绩以及北朝的艺术成就和复杂特性。

图22
彩绘陶牛，具有活泼模塑和眼部内外的生动彩绘，北齐 (550-577)，
Norman A. Kurland 收藏。(目录编号38)

图23 a, b, c
a. 附于珠饰纹带的狮头以及挂置牛臀上的饰带，陶制并含有鲜明颜料和鎏金痕迹，
Norman A. Kurland 收藏。(目录编号38)
b. 青铜狮兽面具，Norman A. Kurland 收藏。
c. 彩绘陶马 北齐 (550-577)，Norman A. Kurland 收藏。

脚注

1 虽然情况有所改变，鲜卑尽管在中国历史中有其重要性，但于英语学界里相对来说仍较为陌生。参阅 Charles Holcombe 的研究 'The Xianbei in Chinese History,' *Early Medieval China* 19 (2013), p. 1.

2 汉唐帝国之间四百年的适当名称仍持续困扰着学者，对于非专家来说亦感迷惑。大幅分裂和政权变迁导致留下相当无法令人满意的选择：如「三国、西晋、南北朝」或「三国六朝」亦或是南方版本的「六朝」。此处简示的「六朝」是指吴国加上五朝，其皆设都于建康（今南京）。这六个朝代是由汉人统治，因为北方是被「胡人」所掌理，而自视为中国传统的唯一合法标准承继者。四十多年前西方历史学家曾试图把这段期间称为中国的「黑暗时代」。直至今日，历史学家经常指称这段政治复杂跨度为早期中世纪中国，但我个人对此有所保留，因为其意味与西方历史有着平行类比关系。

3 「鲜卑」之名来自现代标准发音，是由早先的中国学者所转译文字而来，并非原来的在地名称。而且最近学者曾试图以发声如「Särbi」来重建其本土原型，但这也只是推测而已。参阅 Holcombe, 'The Xianbei', p. 3.

4 详见 Mark Elliott 的文章 'Hushuo, The Northern Other and the Naming of the Han Chinese,' p. 174, in *Critical Han Studies, The History and Representation and Identity of China's Majority*, edited by Thomas S. Mullaney, James Leibold, Stephane Gros, and Eric Vanden Bussche (Berkeley, Los Angeles, and London: University of California Press, 2012)。他调查「汉」字辞汇的历史和使用，以及其如何被中原人民所应用。

5 参阅 Scott Pearce, Audrey Spiro and Patricia Ebrey, editors. *Culture and Power in the Reconstitution of the Chinese Realm* (Cambridge, MA. and London: Harvard University Asia Center and distributed by Harvard University Press, 2001): Introduction, p. 1.

6 同上注。

7 同上注。Introduction, pp. 18-19.

8 参阅 Lou Lin, 'A Study of the Civilization of the Northern Wei Dynasty in its Founding Period,' *Eurasian Studies*, English Edition IV, editors-in-chief, Yu Taishan & Lin Jinxiu (Asia Publishing Nexus, 2016), pp. 95-97。刘陟在其《南齐书》当中创辟关于北魏（386-534）的篇章之卷56《幸臣传》与卷57《魏虏传》。

9 同上注，p. 101 与 Elliott, 'Hushuo', p. 180；根据 W.F. J. Jenner, *Memories of Luoyang, Yang Hsüan-chih and the lost capital (493-534)* (Oxford: Clarendon Press, 1981), p. 86，六朝时期文本中的「胡」字辞汇，几乎总是指西方人种（一般来自印度和泛印中亚）或是称具有高鼻髭髯的其他人群。在中国边界和周遭而与汉地文化有所往来的游牧部落，通常被视为羯、羯胡和柔然与其他名称。

10 J. Holmgren 在她极为有趣又具启发的文章 'Northern Wei as a Conquest Dynasty: Current Perceptions; Past Scholarship,' *Papers on Far Eastern History* 40 (September 1989), pp. 1-3，讨论导致西方对北魏史忽略的诸多因素。这种轻视在某种程度上源于传统中国对北魏的看法，其视之为征服朝代而不具合法性，在善意淡化、沉默尴尬或敌视仇忾的态度之间交替变化。

11 Alexander C. Soper 的文章 'South Chinese Influence on the Buddhist Art of the Six Dynasties Period,' *Bulletin of the Museum of Far Eastern Antiquities* 32 (1960), pp. 50-56 之重要分析，在于通过连接文献证据的断简残篇和来自四川的有限佛教出土文物，进而提出非凡的见解看法。然而，他的文章之附标题名「北方的黑暗时代」(The Dark Ages in the North) 却对游牧民族有所偏见。许多历史学家也承认游牧民族与汉人之间模糊不清的界线区隔，这是因为在社会各个层面中，相互融合过程并不均衡地发展进行：参阅 Holcombe, 'The Xianbei', pp. 22-29；Mark Edward Lewis, *China Between Empires, The Northern and Southern Dynasties* (Cambridge, MA. and London, England: The Belknap Press of Harvard University Press, 2009), p. 168; Pearce, Spiro and Ebrey, *Culture*, Introduction, pp. 1-35.

12 参阅 Thomas J. Barfield, *The Perilous Frontier* (Cambridge, MA : B. Blackwell, 1989).

13 参阅 David B. Honey, 'Sinification as Statecraft in Conquest Dynasties of China: Two Medieval Case Studies,' *Journal of Asian History* 30.2 (1996), p. 116.

14 详见 Mark Elliott, 'Hushuo', pp. 181-182 和 Susan Bush, 'Thunder Monsters, Auspicious Animals, and Floral Ornaments in Early Sixth-Century China,' *Ars Orientalis* X (1975), pp. 19-33; Lewis, *China Between Empires*, pp. 167-168.

15 关于五世纪铺首的图像变异，从叶饰纹样到幼年佛陀与西亚神祇的跨度发展需要深入研究，这部份我将在来日着手进行。与此相似的叶饰树样面具，亦被发现于大同湖东五世纪晚期的1号墓里。这是自司马金龙墓被发掘后，所出现的大型墓葬之一。参阅山西大同市考古研究所，《大同湖东北魏一号墓》，《文物》2004年12期，页 26-34；页 29：图5。近年来，大同市东部和南部已发掘超过三百座的北魏墓葬。在 Kurland 收藏中单件大型铺首之上的这位女性神祇，有可能是娜娜女神的形象，其动物标志为狮子，经常在手中各自持有日月。

16 有关甘肃宁夏螺祖庙出土的铺首，参阅 Annette L. Juliano and Judith A. Lerner, *Monks and Merchants, Silk Road Treasures from Northwest China, Gansu and Ningxia, 4th - 7th Century* (New York: Harry N. Abrams, Inc. with the Asia Society, 2001), pp. 83-84, figs. 17a, b; 18a, b; 至于大同宋绍祖墓石棺与其外饰雕刻铺首，参阅 Annette L. Juliano, *Unearthed, Recent Archaeological Finds from Northern China* (Williamstown, MA: Sterling and Francine Clark Art Museum distributed by Yale University Press, 2012), pp. 43-46；而从M1墓新出的一对鎏金铜铺首，其间人物握持龙颈之例，详见 Chen Yongzhi 陈永志, Song Guodong 宋国栋, and Ma Yan 马艳, 'The Results of the Excavation of the Yihe-Nur Cemetery in Zhenxiangbai Banner (2012-2014),' *The Silk Road* 14 (2016), p. 47.

17 参阅 Wu Hung, 'Buddhist Elements in Early Chinese Art (2nd to 3rd. C.A.D.)' *Artibus Asiae* Vol. XLVI, 3/4 (1986), pp. 269-270, figs. 11, 12。巫鸿认为这个图式是源自于「豢龙氏」的中国神话，在此图式被采用至中国图汇后而所有联系。屈志仁则指出此与在喀布尔阿富汗国家博物馆收藏、来自该国北部黄金之丘的一件约西元前一世纪之镶嵌石榴石、青金石和绿松石的鎏金缀饰有所关系，属于遥远西方的前身范例，之后作为一种图式而可能从草原生活的早期鲜卑文化中存留下来。参阅 James C.Y. Watt, *Dawn of a Golden Age, 200-750 AD* (New York: Metropolitan Museum of Art and New Haven and London: Yale University Press, 2004), pp. 9-10, fig. 7；在该书 p. 164, no. 73 中的作品，其内蒙出土前例即为 no. 35，可能与大夏有关。亦详见 Juliano and Lerner, *Monks and Merchants*, pp. 83-84, figs. 17a, b; 18a, b.

18 参阅 Juliano, *Unearthed*, pp. 35-53；关于发掘报告部份，参阅山西省考古研究所与大同市考古研究所，《大同市北魏宋绍祖墓发掘简报》，《文物》2001年7期，页 19-39.

19 参阅 Juliano and Lerner, *Monks and Merchants*, p. 79, fig. D，司马金龙（卒于484年）墓中两个小型石基的纹饰拓片。

20 带有鸟饰的三足铜盆类似于 Kurland 所藏大型铺首的外缘边饰，参见Chen, Song, and Ma, 'The Results of the Excavation of the Yihe-Nur Cemetery,' p. 52, fig. 32.

21 Jessica Rawson 和 Suzanne Valenstein 都曾在其北朝华丽贴花陶瓷的研究中讨论过此种关键联系，详见 Jessica Rawson, 'Central Asian Silver and Its Influence on Chinese Ceramics,' *Bulletin of the Asia Institute*, 5 (1991): pp. 139-151 和 Suzanne G. Valenstein, *Cultural Convergence in the Northern Qi Period: A Flamboyant Chinese Ceramic Container, A Research Monograph* (New York: The Metropolitan Museum of Art, Asian Art Department, 2007), pp. 63-71.

22 在辽宁及内蒙中皆发掘出铁制马镫的考古证据。为了战斗和射击，此类马镫为马鞍座位提供稳定性，并加上全副装甲的马匹，营造一个着实强大的鲜卑骑兵部队。参阅 Holcombe, 'The Xianbei', pp. 21-22。关于出土于辽宁北票冯素弗墓的马镫，详见黎瑶渤，《辽宁北票县官营子北燕冯素弗墓》，《文物》1973年3期，页2-28；图43 (马镫)；铁制马镫亦出版于 Watt, *Dawn*, p. 130, no. 41.

23 参阅 Holcombe, 'The Xianbei', pp. 20, 23.

24 同上注，pp. 19-20；参阅 Lewis, *China Between Empires*, p. 114；Mark Lewis 也指出除了少数例外，几乎所有非汉族的中国王朝，都在其首都旁强制安置数千人民，来从事畜牧业和农业，为国家与军队提供服务， p. 138.

25 参阅 Soper, 'South Chinese Influence', p. 53.

26 参阅 Annette L. Juliano, *Buddhist Sculpture from China, Selections from the Xi'an Beilin Museum Fifth Through Ninth Centuries* (New York: China Institute Gallery, 2007), p. 4.

27 参阅 Elliott, 'Hushuo', p. 181.

28 参阅 Soper, 'South Chinese Influence', p. 56 和 Holcombe, 'The Xianbei', p. 24.

29 详见 Nancy Shatzman Steinhardt 对城市规划和建筑发展的描述，*Chinese Architecture in an Age of Turmoil, 200-600* (Honolulu: University of Hawai'i Press and Hong Kong University Press, 2014), p. 35.

30 参阅 Soper, 'South Chinese Influence,' p. 51.

31 这五尊云冈巨佛是向前任皇帝和先祖纪念致意。参阅 Alexander C. Soper, 'Imperial Cave-Chapels of the Northern Dynasties: Donor, Beneficiaries, Dates,' *Artibus Asiae*, Vol. XXVII.4 (1966), pp. 242-243。就《南齐书》中对平城的描述指出，在南门之外有五座寺庙以对应其五代先祖，详见 Lou Lin, 'A Study of the Civilization of the Northern Wei,' p. 97.

32 参阅 Soper, 'Beneficiaries, Dates,' pp. 241-246.

33 参阅 Los Angeles County Museum of Art, Overseas Archaeological Exhibition Corporation, The People's Republic of China, *The Quest for Eternity* (San Francisco: Chronicle Books, 1987), Nos. 47-49. (司马金龙)

34 针对游牧民族和汉人之间文化融合的杰出讨论，详见 David B. Honey, 'Stripping off Felt and Fur: An Essay on Nomadic Sinification,' *Paper on Inner Asia 21*(1992), pp. 1-39。中国历史连续性对外族所建立的王朝和统治总有欠公允。Honey 的文章旨在平衡传统汉族中心论对游牧民族或胡人历史诠释的偏见，「其低估了异族血统之时代倾注的影响力」(p. 3).

35 尽管许多汉人逃离鲜卑转往南方，但其他人仍依旧使用鲜卑姓氏和服饰，并选择军武生涯，而非依靠关系来固守其民事地位。参阅 Elliott, 'Hushuo' pp. 180-182.

36 参阅 Holcombe, 'The Xianbei', p. 14; Lewis, *China Between Empires*, p. 81.

37 有关深藏于私人宅邸、寺院和庙宇的园林描述，详见 W.F.J. Jenner, *Memories of Loyang*, pp. 173; 241-244 和杨衒之《洛阳伽蓝记》，王伊同 (Yi-t'ung Wang) 英译 (Princeton, New Jersey: Princeton University Press, 1984), pp. 58-59; 191-196.

38 参阅 Jenner, *Memories*, p. 104.

39 参阅 Lewis, *China Between Empires*, p. 115.

40 参阅 Jenner, *Memories*, p. 56.

41 同上注, p. 12.

42 参阅 Albert E. Dien, *Six Dynasties Civilization* (New Haven and London: Yale University Press, 2007), p. 315 和 Annette L. Juliano, 'Buddhist Sculpture: Innovation, Invention, and Imagination,' in *Art in a Time of Chaos, Masterworks from Six Dynasties China 3rd - 6th Centuries*, Willow Weilan Hai, Annette L. Juliano, Gong Liang, Shi Jinming, and Bai Ning (New York: China Institute Gallery, 2016), p. 104.

43 参阅 Juliano and Lerner, *Monks and Merchants*, p. 136.

44 由于北魏在520年左右开始衰退，第二个石窟寺群便于洛阳东侧开凿。巩县石窟虽无浩大场景，但仍令人印象深刻，特别是最大型的1号窟。这座窟寺是由富裕和权势的赞助者支持，有着精美的天顶藻井，并附带莲花化生、天人和皇家礼佛图。在 Kurland 收藏中有件小型浮雕，有可能就是描绘原来皇家礼佛图中一部份的随从人员 (目录编号21)。虽然该件展示线性北魏风格的典型特征，但其人物样式仍略显固实，详见河南省文物局文物工作队，《巩县石窟》(北京:文物出版社)，第1窟，图版8-57乃是佛陀壁龛上方所绘拱门的精彩叶饰。

45 参阅 Soper, 'South Chinese Influence,' pp. 47-112，另一个略有不同的观点则见于 Angela Falco Howard, 'From the Han to the Southern Song,' in *Chinese Sculpture*, by Angela Falco Howard, Li Sung, Wu Hung, and Yang Hong. *Chinese Sculpture* (New Haven and London: Yale University Press and Beijing: Foreign Languages Press, 1995), p. 236.

46 马匹在中国文化中已获得重要地位。Henry Serruys, C.I.C.M, 'A Note on China's Northern Frontier,' *Monumenta Serica*. 28 (1969), p. 451，其指出在三国时期，游牧民族相当意识到汉族对于马匹的需要，而决定不再出售更多马匹藉以获得妥协让步，而造成汉族官员极大的烦恼。

47 参阅 Juliano, *Unearthed*, pp. 105-106, figs. 2-3，有些五世纪晚期的陶制墓葬雕塑出自于在大同近郊出土的宋绍祖 (卒于477年) 墓，而部份则来自大同雁北师院的五个北魏墓群，详见 Watt, *Dawn*, pp. 142-143, nos. 51, 52, 以及大同出土的司马金龙墓, p. 161, fig. 70; 洛阳博物馆，《洛阳北魏元邵墓》，《考古》1973年4期，页218-224、243 和 图版8-12；若比较从洛阳元邵墓六世纪早期案例至大同司马金龙墓六世纪晚期作品，即可见到大同陶制墓葬雕塑的风格改变。

48 参阅 Lewis, *China Between Empires*, p.83 和 Holcombe, 'The Xianbei', p. 30.

49 现有许多关于青州发现文物的出版品，也许最易入手者为 *Return of the Buddha*, pl. 8-10.

50 参阅 王华庆，《青州隆兴寺佛教造像艺术》(山东:山东出

Shanxi sheng kaogu yanjiu suo 山西省考古研究所 [Shanxi Provincial Archaeology Institute] and Datong shi kaogu yanjiu suo 大同市考古研究所 [Datong City Archaeological Research Institute], 'Datong shi Bei Wei Song Shaozu mu fajue baogao' 大同市北魏宋绍祖墓发掘简报 [Brief Report of Song Shaozu's Northern Wei tomb, Datong City], *Wenwu* 文物, 7 (2001), pp. 19-39.

Soper, Alexander C. 'Imperial Cave-Chapels of the Northern Dynasties: Donor, Beneficiaries, Dates,' *Artibus Asiae*, Vol. XXVII, 4 (1966), pp. 241-270.

Soper, Alexander C. 'South Chinese Influence on the Buddhist Art of the Six Dynasties Period,' *Bulletin of the Museum of Far Eastern Antiquities 32* (1960), pp. 47-107.

Steinhardt, Nancy Shatzman. *Chinese Architecture in an Age of Turmoil, 200-600*. Honolulu: University of Hawai'i Press and Hong Kong University Press, 2014.

Tianshui Maijishan shiku yishu yanjiusuo bian, 天水麦积山石窟艺术研究所编 [Edited by the Art Institute of the Maijishan Grottoes, Tianshui], *Zhongguo shiku Tianshui Maijishan* 中国石窟天水麦积山 [*The Grotto Art of China, The Maijishan Grottoes, Tianshui*], Beijing: Wenwu chubanshe, 1998.

Valenstein, Suzanne G. *Cultural Convergence in the Northern Qi Period: A Flamboyant Chinese Ceramic Container, A Research Monograph*. New York: The Metropolitan Museum of Art, Asian Art Department, 2007.

Wang Huaqing ed., 王华庆, *Qingzhou Longxingsi fojiao zaoxiang yishu* 青州龙兴寺佛教造像艺术 [*Buddhist Imagery at Longxing Temple of Qingzhou*], Shandong: Shandong chubanshe, 1999.

Watt, James C.Y. *Dawn of a Golden Age, 200-750 AD*. New York: Metropolitan Museum of Art and New Haven and London: Yale University Press, 2004.

Wu Hung, 'Buddhist Elements in Early Chinese Art (2nd to 3rd. C. A.D.)' *Artibus Asiae*, Vol. XLVI, 3/4 (1986), pp. 263-303; 305-352.

Wu Hung 巫鸿, *Han Tang zhi jian de zongjiao yishu yu kaogu* 汉唐之间的宗教艺术与考古 [*Between Han and Tang: Religious Art and Archaeology in a Transformative Period*], Beijing: Wenwu chubanshe, 2000; *Han Tang zhijian de wenhua yishu de hudong yu jiaorong* 汉唐之间的文化艺术的互动与交融 [*Between Han and Tang : Cultural and Artistic Interaction in a Transformative Period*], Beijing: Wenwu chubanshe, 2001; *Han Tang zhi jian de shijue wenhua yu wuzhi wenhua* 汉唐之间的视觉文化与物质文化 [*Between Han and Tang: Visual and Material Culture in a Transformative Period*], Beijing: Wenwu chubanshe, 2003.

Yang Hsüan-chih, *A Record of Buddhist Monasteries in Lo-yang*, translated by Yi-t'ung Wang, Princeton, New Jersey: Princeton University Press, 1984.

Zhonghua shiji tan yishu guan 中华世纪坛艺术馆 [China Millenium Monument Art Museum] and Qingzhou shi Bowuguan 青州市博物馆 [Qingzhou Municipal Art Museum], editors. *Qingzhou Beichao fojiao zaoxiang* 青州北朝佛教造像 [*Northern Dynasties Buddhist Images from Qingzhou*]. Beijing: Wenwu chubanshe, 2002.

Catalogue

Six Dynasties art from the
Norman A. Kurland collection

*Part one*

*Left* catalogue number 35
**Painted and Gilt Marble Stele** (detail)
Northern Qi period, 550 - 577
Height: 65.0cm

# 1
## Green-glazed Stoneware Tripod Censer (lian)
Three Kingdoms or Western Jin Period, 3rd Century
Yueyao kilns, Zhejiang province
Height: 9.7cm
Diameter: 14.7cm

Olive-green-glazed grey stoneware circular tripod censer with high sides, supported on three feet, each modelled in the form of a crouching bear with large ears, prominent snout and furry pelt. The vessel is encircled by a central cross-hatched band, decorated with moulded appliqués: three are of small figures of Buddha on a lotus throne alternating with mythical animals, two of winged single-horned *qilin* and two of a double-headed beast. The central register is enclosed by a raised upper border of stamped circular florets and a plain raised lower border. The entire vessel, including the slightly concave base, is covered with a pale olive-green glaze.

Provenance:

J. J. Lally & Co., New York.

Norman A. Kurland, U. S. A.

Exhibited:

Princeton, New Jersey, 1999, Princeton University Art Museum.

Similar examples:

'Tombs of the Eastern Wu State at Datangling, Sheng County, Zhejiang', *Kaogu*, volume 3, Beijing, 1991, plate 1, figure 4 for an example with cover, decorated with Buddha figures and masks, discovered in a tomb dated to 263; also, Zhu Boqian ed., *The Complete Works of Chinese Ceramics*, volume 4, Shanghai, 2000, page 52, plate 18; also, Stanley K. Abe, *Ordinary Images*, Chicago, 2002, figure 2 46.

S. Mizuno, *Tenri sankokan toroku; chugoku hen*, (Pictorial Guide to the Tenri Museum; Chinese Section), Tokyo and Osaka, 1967, plate 174 for an example decorated with masks and riders on mythical creatures; also, Mayuyama & Co. Ltd, *Mayuyama, Seventy Years*, volume 1, Tokyo, 1976, plate 86; also, Tenri University Sankokan Museum, *Tenri hizo meihin-ten*, (Exhibition of Masterworks from the Tenri Museum), Osaka, 1992, page 101, plate 334.

The sprig-moulded motifs on this censer are characteristic of Yueyao vessels of this period. However, the combination showing Buddha alternating with mythical animals, possibly of Daoist origin, is unusual. Figures of Buddha on Yue wares are amongst the very early images of the deity in China, perhaps functioning as auspicious symbols, like the mythical animals, rather than as specific representations for worship. Figures of Buddha are also found on the celadon-glazed 'granary jars' of the Eastern Wu period: these three-dimensional appliqué figures, along with those of birds, animals and buildings, are arranged around the upper sections of large vessels. After the third century, the use of the Buddha image as a decorative motif became less common in the south of China, whereas in the north, from around the fourth century, the image of Buddha began to take on an iconic, rather than decorative significance.[1]

[1] Albert E. Dien, *Six Dynasties Civilization*, New Haven and London, 2007, pages 399 - 400, as well as pages 387 - 420 for a more general discussion of the introduction and spread of Buddhism during the Six Dynasties period.

一

青釉陶奁

越窑 浙江

三国或西晋 公元三世纪

高 九·七公分

直径 一四·七公分

青釉灰石胎，瓷体圆形，筒壁高直，三足支撑，足为蜷熊型，大耳凸吻，毛发遍体。炉壁外中部饰带一周，镶有贴饰，含三尊莲台佛像，间饰神兽纹，有单角带翼麒麟与双头兽各一对。中心带上下，各饰一圈凸带纹，上带印有圆圈纹，下带素纹。包括略凹的底部，整器施以浅青釉。

## 2
## Gilt-bronze Buddha

*Northern Wei period, inscribed with date corresponding to 482*
*Height: 27.0cm*

Cast gilt-bronze figure of Shakyamuni seated in *virasana* on a squared Sumeru throne, supported on a four-legged pedestal, with right hand raised in *abhaya mudra* and left hand holding his garment. He wears monastic robes with beaded borders covering both shoulders and most of the undergarment, leaving the torso partially exposed, the end cascading over the left shoulder, and falling in fine pleats across the body and the legs. His rounded face bears a contemplative expression, with narrowed eyes beneath arched brows and his hair, tightly curled in whorls, covers the prominent *ushnisha*. The back of the figure is flat with two lugs for the insertion of the detachable mandorla. The leaf-shaped mandorla is cast in low relief with a central halo containing a lotus bloom encircled by a lotus scroll, itself surmounted by a figure of Buddha on a lotus throne, flanked by flying *apsaras* holding streamers and pendant jewels. The waisted throne is decorated with wavy lines, petals, dot and criss-cross patterns and the pedestal legs are cast with foliate scrolls and fronds at the front and sides, the back incised with an eighty-four character inscription. Much of the gilding remains on the figure, with areas of malachite patination.

Provenance:

Private collection.

Eskenazi Limited, London.

Norman A. Kurland, U. S. A.

Published:

Sotheby's, New York, *The Arts of the Buddha*, 22 September 2004, number 4.

Giuseppe Eskenazi in collaboration with Hajni Elias, *A Dealer's Hand, The Chinese Art Market Through the Eyes of Giuseppe Eskenazi*, London, 2012, page 211, plate 91.

Similar examples:

S. Matsubara, *A History of Chinese Buddhist Sculpture*, Tokyo, 1995, plates volume 1, plate 63a for an example without mandorla excavated in 1977 in Yenqing county, Beijing, now in the Capital Museum, Beijing (inscribed but date illegible).

S. Matsubara, *A History of Chinese Buddhist Sculpture*, Tokyo, 1995, plates volume 1, plate 71a, for a figure dated to 484 excavated from Togeton, Hohhot, Inner Mongolia, now in the Inner Mongolia Region Museum; also, James Watt et al., *China, Dawn of a Golden Age, 200 - 750 AD*, New York, 2004, number 76.

The Nelson-Atkins Museum of Art, *A Handbook of the Collection*, Kansas City, 2008, page 310, figure 89 for a similar example lacking its throne and pedestal.

Hugo Münsterberg, 'Buddhist Bronzes of the Six Dynasties Period', *Artibus Asiae*, volume IX, 4, Ascona, 1946, plate 7, for the example dated 484 now in the Fogg Museum, Harvard; also, Ulrich von Schroeder, *Indo-Tibetan Bronzes*, Hong Kong, 1981, figure 141D; also, Kristin A. Mortimer, *Harvard University Art Museums, A Guide to the Collections*, New York, 1985, number 18; also, Leopold Swergold, *Thoughts on Chinese Buddhist Gilt Bronzes*, Connecticut, 2014, object 2.

二

鎏金铜佛坐像　北魏　太和年铭

应为公元四八二年

高 二七·〇公分

鎏金铜质，释迦摩尼佛，结跏趺坐于方形须弥台，下承四腿基座。佛右手抬起施无畏印，左手握衣襟。身穿袈裟，珠纹镶边，覆盖双肩

及僧祇支，前胸半敞，外衣翻过左肩，垂皱覆盖身体和腿部。佛面表情肃穆，弯眉细目，发呈涡纹肉髻。像背平坦，有两构件，为安装活动覆盖双肩

背光而置。叶形背光，浅浮雕式，头光居中，莲花怒放，莲茎环绕，上有佛坐莲台，两侧飞天，手持飘带和垂璎。束腰台座沿饰以波纹，花

瓣纹，点纹和交叉纹，基座腿部铸成枝叶纹饰，正面和侧面为复叶纹。座背刻有铭文八十四字。此像鎏金大都保存，有部分孔雀石结层。

The inscription on the pedestal reads as follows:

太和六年正月十七日 夫至腊，玄原非想，佛所到训顾积载之敬，众神化之终始，是以清信女惠可，自惟贸缘，犹生不靓，今为余过，可祚法媚，造释迦大佛一区，缘此微初，使王者不恋三途八上之像，直至成佛，普同斯愿

which may be translated as:

The seventeenth day of the first month of the sixth year of the Taihe reign [corresponding to 482]. A year has ended. We are honoured that Buddha has inspired and directed us for many years; we have been eternally blessed. Female devotee Hui Ke, fated to live a difficult life, perhaps through her fault, asks for Buddha's blessing and respectfully has had a sculpture of Shakyamuni Buddha made in the hope that, from now on, the ruler and all living beings avoid an evil fate and forever be spared temptation, until they become one with Buddha.

The similar examples from various museum collections cited above closely resemble the present gilt-bronze in the modelling of Buddha's hair and face and in the diagonal cascading arrangement of the robes. Another common feature is the waisted Sumeru throne, representing the central axis of the Buddhist universe, linking the physical and spiritual worlds, but the present sculpture is unusual in that it lacks the pair of guardian lions seated at the edge of throne. The depiction of Buddha in this pose of 'preaching the law' (Fo shuo fa), with right hand raised, seems to have been an important visual image of this period, seen across the different media of stone and bronze.

The high quality of the casting on the present figure is notable in the fine pleats of the drapery, the refined features of the face and the detailed foliate motifs on the throne, testifying to the fact that the Taihe reign (477 - 499) during the latter half of the Northern Wei period, was 'marked by an impressive production of gilt bronzes, especially in the north-eastern provinces of Shanxi and Hebei at the heart of the Xianbei dominance.'[1] Both the examples from Hohhot, Inner Mongolia and from the Fogg cited above, were also produced during the Taihe reign and are dated to 484, two years after the present figure was cast.

[1] James Watt et al., China, Dawn of a Golden Age, 200 - 750 AD, New York, 2004, pages 167 - 168.

## 3
## Bronze Seated Maitreya
Northern Wei period, inscribed with date corresponding to 494
Height: 13.1cm

Cast bronze figure of Maitreya seated on a rectangular stool with knees apart and feet on the ground in the 'European' position (*pralambapadasana*) with hands in *abhaya* and *varada mudra*, on a Sumeru throne, supported by a four-legged pedestal. The deity has a finely modelled face with narrowed eyes, long ears and lips forming an 'archaic' smile. His hair, with curls indicated by punched circles, is neatly arranged over the prominent *ushnisha*. He is dressed in monastic robes with ring-punched borders, draped across the chest and around the shoulders and cascading in narrow pleats over the left arm and between the legs. The flat back of the figure is undecorated except for two squared loops, probably for the attachment of a mandorla. Borders of rope twist, cross-hatch and pendant petals decorate the pedestal, the front legs cast with a pair of monks dressed in flowing robes, each with arm raised towards a censer or *boshanlu* between them. To the proper left side, a pair of figures, each dressed in a tall hat and long tunic over trousers, face each other bearing a lotus bloom aloft, their stems entwined. On the proper right side, the pedestal is cast with a leafy scroll above stylized flower-heads. The reverse of the pedestal is incised with an inscription of approximately seventy-one characters. The bronze has a rich greenish patina with minor encrustation.

### Provenance:

J. J. Lally and Co., New York.

Norman A. Kurland, U. S. A.

### Exhibited:

Princeton, New Jersey, 1999, Princeton University Art Museum.

### Similar examples:

S. Matsubara, *A History of Chinese Buddhist Sculpture*, Tokyo, 1995, plates volume 1, plates 97a and b for two views of a Shakyamuni Buddha of similar size; and plates 96a and b for two slightly larger figures.

三

铜坐式弥勒佛像　北魏　太和年铭　应为公元四九四年

高　一三·一公分

铜铸弥勒佛像，坐于长方形凳上，双膝分开，两脚踏地，呈善跏趺坐式，手施无畏与愿印，须弥台下，基座四腿支撑。弥勒塑造精致，像背无饰纹，有两个方形环扣，或为安装背光之用。座台绳纹上沿，束腰处菱纹，座周俯莲瓣纹，前支柱各饰一和尚，身穿僧衣，举手趋向中间的博山

细目长耳，唇呈微笑，圆印螺发，肉髻高耸。身着袈裟，环纹饰边，衣袍抱肩过胸，细褶垂流，盖于左臂，散落在两腿之间。

The inscription on the reverse of the pedestal reads as follows:

太和十八七月六日弟子万凤，引后夫，引为 □，俟吕陵豆，伏贡造佛像一躯，并为夫 □ 产父母 □ 七 □ 世父前因后 □ □ □ 愿造因缘 □ □ □ 写马七珍 □ □ □ 禾田 □ 愿 □ □ □ 池 □ □

which may be partially translated as:

On the sixth day of the seventh month of the eighteenth year of the Taihe reign [corresponding to 494], the disciples, Wan Feng, Yin Houfu, Yin Wei □, Qilüling Dou, respectfully commissioned a statue of Buddha, for their parents, for seven generations....

The present figure is unusual in that Buddha is shown seated with both feet placed on the ground, in the so-called 'European' position or *pralambapadasana*. This posture is often associated with the Historical Buddha, and sometimes with Maitreya, considered to be both a bodhisattva and the Buddha of the Future. In the latter case, the deity is said to be in this pose so that he can readily stand in preparation for his descent into the world as the next Buddha.

炉。铜像左侧，一对戴高帽的，长袍过膝，面目相对，手持莲花蕾，莲茎缠绕。在右侧有抽象的花蕾纹，上饰枝叶纹。器背有铭文，刻有七十一字。通体布满厚实的绿锈，少部有锈层。

4

## Sandstone Head and Shoulders of Buddha

Northern Wei period, mid to late 5th century
Yungang cave temples, Shanxi province
Height: 43.3cm
Width: 31.5cm

Large sandstone Buddha, comprising head, neck and proper left shoulder. The Buddha's face is delicately carved with high cheek-bones, arched brows framing eyes half-closed in contemplation, a well-formed nose and elongated ears. His small mouth is set in an 'archaic smile' above a cleft chin. The hair is neatly arranged in a straight line across his forehead and drawn up over the prominent *ushnisha*. His chest is partially exposed beneath the monastic robes edged with narrow raised borders. The weathered sandstone is of a beige tone.

Provenance:

Yungang cave temples, Shanxi province.

Yamanaka Co. Ltd., Tokyo (acquired 1930 - 1935), by repute.

Atsuji Shibusawa (1872 - 1942), adopted son of Eiichi Shibusawa.

Keizo Shibusawa (1896 - 1963) (served as Japanese Minister of Finance after the Second World War), from whom by descent.

Senshutey, Tokyo.

Eskenazi Limited, London.

Norman A. Kurland, U. S. A.

Exhibited:

Possibly Osaka, 1934, Osaka Arts Society.

London, 2014, Eskenazi Limited.

Published:

By repute, Yamanaka and Osaka Arts Society, *Grand Exhibition of Ancient Chinese and Korean Works of Art*, Tokyo, 1934, number 357 (unillustrated).

Eskenazi Limited, *Chinese sculpture c. 500 - 1500*, London, 2014, number 1.

Giuseppe Eskenazi in collaboration with Hajni Elias, *A Dealer's Hand, The Chinese Art Market Through the Eyes of Giuseppe Eskenazi*, (Chinese edition), Shanghai, 2015, page 358, plate 446.

Similar examples:

Seiichi Mizuno and Toshio Nagahiro, *Yun-Kang: The Buddhist Cave-Temples of the Fifth Century A.D. in North China*, volume 12, Kyoto, 1954, plates 82 and 86 for Buddha figures from niches of the east reveal of the window in Cave 18; also, Su Bai and Li Zhiguo ed., *Zhongguo meishu quanji, diaosu bian 10, Yungang shiku diaoke*, (The Great Treasury of Chinese Art, Sculpture 10, Yungang Caves), Beijing, 1988, page 167, number 161.

四

沙岩佛头肩像　北魏　公元五世纪中晚期

云冈石窟　山西　高 四三·三公分　宽 三一·五公分

砂岩佛像，体型较大，含头颈及左肩。佛面雕工细致，高颧弯眉，双眼半睐，呈沉思状，鼻形挺直，长耳垂肩，小嘴露笑，下巴微隆。发型梳理整洁，额前平齐，上敛成高肉髻。佛着僧衣，前胸半敞，襟领细而凸。经年风化，砂岩显出斑驳的米黄色。

From the mid-fifth century in China, the carving of Buddhist cave temples flourished and, in north China, Yungang was the first imperially sponsored cave temple of the Northern Wei period. Atoning for the persecution of Buddhism by his predecessor, Emperor Wencheng reinstated the Buddhist faith in 452/3 in the north and ordered five cave temples to be built at Yungang. These five cave temples are the earliest on the site (Caves 16, 17, 18, 19 and 20) and are known collectively as *Tanyao wuku*, ('The Five Caves of Tanyao' or 'The Imperial Five'). Tanyao was the chief monk who, in 460, was appointed by the emperor to oversee the newly restored Buddhist faith:

> 'T'an-yao told the Emperor that in the pass of Wu-chou west of the capital the rock wall should be excavated so as to open up five caves, in each of which a Buddhist image should be carved. The largest was seventy feet high and the next largest sixty. The sculptured embellishments in their originality and great scale were unique in the world.'[1]

The example in the present exhibition is similar to the seated figures cited above from Cave 18, in the proportions of the head, treatment of the hairline, deeply cleft chin and the comparatively plain robes. The size would also seem to be comparable. There are numerous small figures in niches, as well as several larger figures, such as the ones cited here, remaining around the window and entrance of Cave 18, in various states of preservation, although many more appear to have been lost.

For further discussion of the Yungang cave temples, refer to the essay 'Northern Dynasties (386 - 581): Sculpture in Turbulent Times' by Annette L. Juliano, pages 18 - 20 in the present catalogue.

[1] Alexander Coburn Soper, *Literary Evidence for Early Buddhist Art in China*, Artibus Asiae, Supplementum XIX, Ascona,1959, page 97.

五

彩绘陶四象之龙虎　北魏　公元六世纪早期

长　一九·五公分　一九·六公分

灰陶胎，实心塑造，四象神灵中的龙和虎，青龙代表东方，白虎代表西方。神兽蜷卧，前腿略分，火焰状双翼出自肩头，后腿依于身侧，身体弯曲呈拱形，长卷尾盘绕在脊背上。神兽头部制作精致，细颈支撑，虎头耳小竖立，圆眼短吻，向左警觉。龙头吻长且尖，单角弯曲，环状毛发，凝视右方。两兽大部施以白色，亦有结壳。

5
# Two Painted Earthenware Animals of the Directions
Northern Wei period, early 6th century
Length: 19.5cm and 19.6cm

Two solid grey earthenware animals of the Four Directions, the 'Dragon of the East' and the 'Tiger of the West'. The mythical creatures crouch, each with front legs slightly splayed, wing-like flames shooting from the shoulders, hind legs tucked to the sides of the arched sinuous body and long curled tail with tip arranged in a neat coil on the ridged back. The well-modelled heads are supported on curving, attenuated necks, the tiger with small pricked ears, round eyes and short snout looking alertly to its left while the dragon, with its long, pointed snout, single curved horn and ruff of fur, gazes to its right. Both figures bear considerable areas of white pigment and some encrustation.

Provenance:

Priestley and Ferraro, London.

Norman A. Kurland, U. S. A.

Exhibited:

London, 1999, Priestley and Ferraro.

Princeton, New Jersey, 1999, Princeton University Art Museum.

Published:

Priestley and Ferraro, *Out of Wind and Dust*, London, 1999, number 5.

Similar examples (for the dragon):

Daisy Lion-Goldschmidt and Jean-Claude Moreau-Gobard, *Chinese Art*, Fribourg, 1960, plate 102.

R-Y L. d'Argencé, *Chinese Ceramics in the Avery Brundage Collection*, San Francisco, 1967, plate Xc; also, Annette L. Juliano, *Art of the Six Dynasties, Centuries of Change and Innovation*, New York, 1975, number 7.

Regina Krahl, *Chinese Ceramics from the Meiyintang Collection*, volume 3 (I), London, 2006, number 1163.

The animals representing the four cardinal directions, comprising the White Tiger of the West (*baihu*), the Green Dragon of the East (*qinglong*), the Vermilion Bird of the South (*zhuque*) and the Black Warrior of the North (*xuanwu*), each also with its own assigned colour, element and season, gained widespread acceptance from the Han period and are found in a variety of media, including metalwork, stone and ceramics. The fifth direction corresponded to the centre and was without an animal representative. During the late fifth and early sixth centuries there was a resurgence in the use of these symbols: 'In the North, the four animals are used as major decorative motifs on many Northern Wei epitaph covers and in clay tomb sculpture ...... excavations also confirm the popularity of this theme in the decor of southern tombs.'[1]

[1] Annette L. Juliano, *Teng-Hsien: An Important Six Dynasties Tomb*, Artibus Asiae Supplementum XXXVII, Ascona, 1980, page 36.

## 6
## Painted Earthenware Rooster
Northern Wei period, early 6th century
Height: 20.7cm

Grey earthenware hollow model of a rooster standing on a rectangular base. Its well-modelled, crested head, with beady eyes and sharp curved beak, is turned alertly to the right. The curved neck and body are covered with combed wavy lines - except on part of the back and chest - to suggest feathers. Incised C-shapes and horizontal lines delineate further feathers on the folded wings while those in the luxuriant fanned tail are individually defined. The bird is supported on stout legs that terminate in sharp-clawed feet. The body and head of the bird are covered in a dark red pigment, while the crest, beak, tail and wings are picked out in white.

### Provenance:
Alfred and Ivy Clark, Iver Heath.

Norman A. Kurland, U. S. A.

### Exhibited:
London, 1947, Oriental Ceramic Society.

Princeton, New Jersey, 1998, Princeton University Art Museum.

### Published:
Oriental Ceramic Society, *Chinese Ceramic Figures*, London, 1947, number 18; also, *Transactions of the Oriental Ceramic Society 1946 - 47*, volume 22, London, 1947, page 55, number 18.

Christie's, London, *Fine Chinese Ceramics and Works of Art*, 16 November 1998, number 163.

### Similar examples:
Fujio Koyama ed., *Toki zenshu 9, kan rikucho dogu*, (Encyclopedia of Ceramics 9, Han and Six Dynasties Figures), Tokyo, 1958, number 62.

Annette L. Juliano, *Art of the Six Dynasties, Centuries of Change and Innovation*, New York, 1975, number 46.

Earthenware models of domestic and farm animals such as sheep, ducks, chickens, pigs and dogs were an integral part of Six Dynasties mortuary figures, placed in the tomb to cater to the needs in the afterlife.

六

彩绘陶公鸡

北魏　公元六世纪早期

高 二0·七公分

灰陶胎，空心模，公鸡立于长方形座上。此件制作精细，头顶肉冠，明眸圆目，弯喙尖利，警觉右顾。除了部分的胸背外，颈弯及身体，有波浪纹线覆盖，应为羽毛纹。鸡腿粗壮，双翅收合，上刻划半圆及横线以描绘成羽翼纹，尾部则塑成扇形长翎，栩栩如生。鸡腿粗壮，鸡爪锋利。深红色覆盖身体与头部，鸡冠喙部尾羽和翅膀，均使用白色。

七

彩绘陶玄武

北魏

公元六世纪早期

长一七・六公分

灰陶胎，蛇缠乌龟型，乃天地四象之一，称为黑色玄武，代表北方。乌龟四腿撑开，惟妙惟肖，扁头外探，扭向尾部。龟壳光滑，施红褐色，六角形原纹依稀可见。蛇体绕龟身，从头到尾呈拱形，蛇头被龟尾勒住，蛇口张开。大部分红褐黑绿原色保留完好。

7
## Painted Earthenware 'Black Warrior of the North'
Northern Wei Dynasty, early 6th century
Length: 17.6cm

Grey earthenware figure of a tortoise encircled by a snake, the 'Black Warrior of the North', representing one of the Four Directions. The tortoise stands with protruding, realistically rendered feet, its narrow head turned back towards its tail. Its smooth carapace is painted a dark reddish-brown and retains traces of the original design of hexagons. The snake is encircled around the belly of the tortoise and forms an arch over its back, its head, with open jaws, caught by the tail of the tortoise. Most of the original red, brown, black and green pigments remain.

Provenance:

Dr. N. Wessén, Stockholm.

Eskenazi Limited, London.

Private collection, London.

Eskenazi Limited, London.

Norman A. Kurland, U. S. A.

Exhibited:

London, 1985, Eskenazi Limited.

Published:

Eskenazi Limited, *Twenty five years*, London, 1985, number 23.

Maurizio Scarpari, *Ancient China; Chinese Civilization from the Origins to the Tang Dynasty*, Vercelli, 2000, page 162.

Giuseppe Eskenazi in collaboration with Hajni Elias, *A Dealer's Hand, The Chinese Art Market Through the Eyes of Giuseppe Eskenazi*, London, 2012, page 252, plate 198.

Similar examples:

Hugh Honour, *The Horizon Book of the Arts of China*, New York, 1969, page 39 for the example in the Seattle Art Museum.

Annette L. Juliano, *Art of the Six Dynasties, Centuries of Change and Innovation*, New York, 1975, number 44 for the example in The Princeton University Art Museum.

The tortoise entwined with the snake represents one of the four cardinal directions and is known as the Black Warrior of the North (*xuanwu*), the four quarters together maintaining the harmony of the universe. Traditionally the tortoise was considered by the Chinese to be female and it is encircled by the snake, which acts as its male element; by extrapolation, the combination of the two creatures was a representation of the principle of *yin* and *yang*.

During the Northern Wei period, the ceramic representations of the Black Warrior seem to have taken two forms – one where the snake is tightly coiled around the tortoise's body, such as the example in The Princeton University Art Museum cited above, and another where the snake is coiled around the body before forming an elegantly looping arch over the carapace, such as in the present example. The latter arrangement is also seen on Six Dynasties tomb tiles such as those excavated at Dengxian, Henan province.[1]

[1] Annette L. Juliano, *Teng-Hsien: An Important Six Dynasties Tomb*, Artibus Asiae Supplementum XXXVII, Ascona, 1980, figure 14.

## 8
## Bronze Openwork Monster Mask
Northern Wei period, late 5th century
Height: 11.8cm
Width: 11.2cm

Cast bronze openwork monster mask of square form. The creature has bulging eyes framed by bushy, curling brows above a pronounced beak with stippled dots and pierced nares, from which a ring handle was probably once suspended. On the animal's forehead is a multi-armed deity dressed in a *dhoti*, seated with legs pendant, crossed at the ankles, lotus bud between the feet, one pair of hands on the knees, another pair grasping the necks of the pair of sinuous dragons. The deity wears a diadem encircling the *ushnisha* and the circular halo behind the head is supported in the mouths of the dragons. Curling feathers, plumes and a pair of pointed ears emerge from the sides of the animal mask, forming the borders. The surface of the bronze has a dark green patina and the reverse is undecorated.

Provenance:

J. J. Lally & Co., New York.

Norman A. Kurland, U. S. A.

Exhibited:

Princeton, New Jersey, 1998, Princeton University Art Museum.

Published:

Shi Yan, *Zhongguo diaosushi tulu 2*, (Catalogue cf Chinese Sculpture 2), Shanghai, 1987, page 502, figure 592.

Similar examples:

Jack V. Sewell, *Chinese Art from the Collection of James W. and Marilynn Alsdorf*, The Arts Club of Chicago, Chicago, 1970, number B14.

Osaka Municipal Museum of Art, *Rikucho no bijutsu*, (Arts of the Six Dynasties), Tokyo, 1976, number 163; also, Osaka Municipal Museum of Art, *Rikucho no bijutsu*, (Arts of the Six Dynasties), (Chinese Art Exhibition Series No. 2), Osaka, 1980, page 18, number 2-43.

Michèle Pirazzoli-t'Serstevens, *L'arte per la vita ne!l' Aldilà: Capolavori di arte antica cinese della collezione Meidaozhai*, (Art for the Afterlife: Masterpieces of Chinese Art in the Meidaozhai Ccllection), volume 3, Turin, 2002, number 456.

Annette L. Juliano and Judith A. Lerner, *Monks and Merchants, Silk Road Treasures from Northwest China*, New York, 2002, number 17 for one of a pair of animal masks, dated to the fifth century, excavated at Leizumiao village, Guyuan, Ningxia province, now n the Guyuan Municipal Museum; also, James Watt et al., *China, Dawn of a Golden Age, 200 – 750 AD*, New York, 2004, number 73; also, Daiko Advertising Inc. ed., *China Crossroads of Culture*, Tokyo, 2005, page 81, number 052; for the excavation report see, 'Excavation of the Northern Wei Tomb at Guyuan, Ningxia,' *Wenwu*, volume 6, Beijing, 1984, page 52, figure 19.

八

铜透雕兽面铺首　北魏　公元五世纪晚期

高 一一·八公分　宽 一一·二公分

铜铸件，正方形透雕兽面。兽面上双眼暴凸，浓眉曲卷，喙部突出，点画纹饰，鼻上钻孔，此件曾有悬环。兽面额头有一多臂神祇，身着兜提，两腿垂放，脚踝交叉，中间莲蕾，一对手扶膝盖，另一对手握住两只蟠龙脖子。仙人头戴冠盖，环绕肉髻，圆形头光，由龙嘴固定。兽面两侧卷羽曲毛，加一对尖耳，构成器边。铜器表面有深绿锈迹，背后素纹。

It has been suggested by Annette Juliano that the standing figure in the examples excavated from Guyuan, Ningxia province cited above, is the Infant Buddha, represented by the large head with *ushnisha*, the rounded body and the short *dhoti*.[1] While the figure on the present example has some of these features – such as the plump, almost female, body and the short *dhoti* (and has, in addition, a halo backing the head), it is not shown standing, as the Infant Buddha usually is, but is depicted seated, with pendant legs crossed at the ankles, a posture generally associated with Maitreya. Thus, although there are Buddhist elements associated with the figure on the present mask, the iconography is not completely clear-cut. Juliano has suggested that the Ningxia example, shown grasping a pair of dragons, has been adapted to the Chinese context: 'the Infant Buddha assumes the auspicious role of "Huan Long Shi, the dragon tamer, a famous character in traditional Chinese legend."' Similarly, on the present example, the multi-armed figure is also shown grasping the heads of a pair of dragons. It is likely that the portrayal on this mask also combines Buddhist elements with that of a traditional deity such as Huan Long Shi, in order to maximise the auspicious potential of both.

[1] Annette L. Juliano and Judith A. Lerner, *Monks and Merchants, Silk Road Treasures from Northwest China*, New York, 2002, numbers 17 and 18.

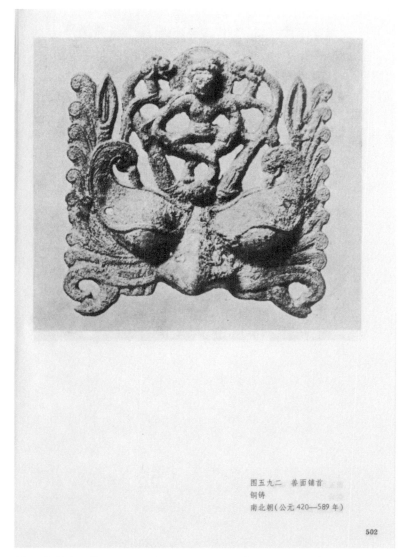

图五九二  兽面铺首
铜铸
南北朝（公元 420—589 年）

502

After Shi Yan, *Zhongguo diaosushi tulu 2*, (Catalogue of Chinese
Sculpture 2), Shanghai, 1987, page 502, figure 592.

九

鎏金铜透雕铺首衔环一对　北魏　公元五世纪晚期

每件高　一三・三公分

每件宽　一三・七公分

每只环直径　九・五公分

鎏金铜质，透雕兽面一对，正方形，高浮雕式，配有鎏金环。兽面上眉浓如盖，双眸紧盯，尖喙突出，上嘴露齿，犬牙龇出。喙底有单钩，为悬挂之用。额上有五叶棕榈冠，两旁枝叶纹饰起自额前，在兽面与尖长耳之侧，弯羽纹为界，器背素纹，位于眼部顶端及偏下，有三孔与销子，作为附件。每只环多棱，整器鎏金厚实，部分有孔雀石锈层。

9
## Pair of Gilt-bronze Openwork Masks and Rings
Northern Wei period, late 5th century
Height of each mask: 13.3cm
Width of each mask: 13.7cm
Diameter of each ring: 9.5cm

Pair of gilt-bronze openwork animal masks of square form cast in high relief, each with a gilt-bronze ring. Each mask has heavy-lidded, staring eyes and a pointed beak or nose, above the upper mouth, with a row of even teeth and sharp canines at the corners. A single curved hook emerges from the nose for suspension of the ring. A five-leaf palmette crest, flanked by foliate motifs, rises from the forehead and curling tufts or plumes form borders on either side of the mask and enclose the sharp, elongated ears. The reverse is undecorated. There are three apertures with pins, at the apex and below the eyes, for attachment. Each of the rings is of faceted shape on one side and concave on the reverse. The richly gilt masks and rings bear areas of malachite encrustation.

Provenance:

J. J. Lally and Co., New York.

Norman A. Kurland, U. S. A.

Similar examples:

*Hebeisheng chutu wenwu xuanji* (Selected Cultural Relics Excavated in Hebei Provence), Beijing, 1980, page 179, number 315 for a pair of masks with ring handles excavated in Ding county in 1957, dated Northern Qi.

The Datong Municipal Museum, 'Gilt Bronzes of the Northern Wei Dynasty Unearthed at Datong', *Kaogu*, volume 11, Beijing, 1983, plate 4, figure 1.1, for an example without a ring, one of five of this type of mask excavated in the southern suburbs of Datong.

The Archaeology Institute of Datong City, 'A Brief Excavation Report on Tomb Group of the Northern Wei located in Qili village, Datong, Shanxi province', *Wenwu*, volume 10, Beijing, 2006, page 40, figures 45 and 47 for two of a group excavated at Qili village, Datong.

Johann and Nicola Kritzinger, *The Youxiantang Collection of Chinese Art*, n. p., 2016, pages 24 - 25 for an example without a ring.

Such monster masks (*pushou*) combining avian and bestial elements, such as feathery crests with fangs, rings suspended in their gaping jaws, have been found in pairs or even in multiples in tombs, as in the similar examples cited above. Most clearly had been used in a tomb – probably attached to a sarcophagus - and undoubtedly had a protective function, perhaps to repel evil spirits from the domain of the deceased. This protective role of such masks – in a different medium – is seen most clearly on the stone sarcophagus of Song Shaozu (d. 477), a magistrate who served under Northern Wei rule, discovered in Caofulou village, Datong, Shanxi province. The one hundred-odd carved stone pieces that comprise the sarcophagus are in the form of a traditional 'wooden' building with roof brackets; the walls and doors are carved with twenty-five ring-handled *pushou*, of three different types, each with a different decorative element between the monster's horns, either overlapping triangles representing mountains, or figures or palmette scrolls.[1] While the origins of these monster masks when used as part of tomb furniture are unclear, such masks clearly bear more than a passing relation to the animal handles found on Han period bronze *hu*-shaped vessels and their ceramic counterparts.

For a further discussion of *pushou*, refer to the essay, 'Northern Dynasties (386 - 581): Sculpture in Turbulent Times' by Annette L. Juliano, pages 16 - 17 in the present catalogue.

[1] Annette L. Juliano, *Unearthed, Recent Archaeological Discoveries from Northern China*, Massachusetts, 2012, pages 43 - 45 and catalogue number 1.

# 10
## Two Earthenware Figures
Northern Wei period, early 6th century
Height of each: 74.7cm and 70.0cm

Two large grey earthenware figures of elongated form, each standing with head slightly inclined, one probably a civil official, the other a military dignitary. The civil official is dressed in a collared grown which is secured at the waist with a sash and falls to the ground, leaving the tips of the upturned shoes visible beneath the hem, while his hands are folded at the waist, resting on top of the long sword, enclosed in its scabbard. His face has finely modelled features with mouth set in a half-smile and he wears a tall *longguan* hat. The military dignitary is dressed in *liangdang* armour, comprising breast- and back-plates, connected by straps over the shoulders and fastened at the waist with a corded belt, over a tunic; his baggy trousers, tied below the knees, break over his upturned shoes. The figure wears a small, close-fitting hat, *pingshangze*, on his head and clasps a flask to his waist. The reverse of bcth figures is flat and undecorated, each with four apertures.

Provenance:

Eskenazi Limited, London.

Norman A. Kurland, U. S. A.

Exhibited:

Harvard, Cambridge, Massachusetts, 2000, Harvard University Art Museums.

Similar examples:

Shi Yan, *Zhongguo diaosushi tulu 2*, (Catalogue of Chinese Sculpture 2), Shanghai, 1987, page 462, figure 539, for a figure similar to the present example holding a long sword, excavated from Luoyang, Henan province.

Shih Hsio-Yen et al., *Chinese Art in the Royal Ontario Museum*, Toronto, 1972, number 84, for a military dignitary.

Annette L. Juliano, *Art of the Six Dynasties, Centuries of Change and Innovation*, New York, 1975, number 24, for a pair of figures from The Minneapolis Institute of Art.

一〇

两个灰陶立俑 北魏 公元六世纪早期

高 七四·七公分 七〇·〇公分

灰陶胎，两立姿俑，体态高大修长，头部微敛，应是一文一武。文官穿翻领长袍，系带腰间，袍襟垂地，鞋尖上翘。双手置腰际，按于长剑柄端，剑身入鞘。俑面塑造细腻，嘴呈笑意，头戴籠冠。武将威严，身着两挡甲，胸前背后各佩一片，革带相连，扛于肩头，另结带于腰，佩挂在袍外。下穿宽松裤，膝下系结，翘鞋头现出。此俑头戴平上帻，手握水瓶于腰部。两俑背后平坦无纹，但各有四处孔隙。

The flattened back of the present figures suggest that they would have been placed against the wall in a tomb, their services required by the deceased in the afterlife. They probably represent civil and military officials and one of them wears two-piece armour plates attached by straps over the shoulders - *liangdang* armour - on top of his clothing: 'As is often the case in sixth-century funerary figures, the officials wear a breastplate over the court clothing.... In addition to their administrative responsibilities, civil officials likely served as a type of honor guard for members of the imperial family and the aristocracy.'[1]

As Albert E. Dien has pointed out, this popular form of *liangdang* attire could either be a form of armour or, in fact, two panelled outer garments, in both instances worn over an undergarment.[2] The undergarments on one of these figures comprises a long-sleeved jacket and a pair of trousers, bound below the knee with a strap; the outfit was known as *kuxi* (trousers and jacket). Although the ensemble was intended to be worn on military campaign, this '*kuxi* style came to be the apparel of both military and civil officials even in the south.'[3] The binding straps at the knees and the belt were probably made of felt.

The small close-fitting hat of flattened form, *pingshangze*, worn by one of the figures, was a popular head-dress of the period, fastened with a bow set in the centre. The head-dress on the other – *longguan* or 'basket hat' - was probably made of semi-transparent lacquered horsehair secured at the back with a clasp.

[1] James Watt et al., *China, Dawn of a Golden Age, 200 – 750 AD*, New York, 2004, page 242.

[2] Albert E. Dien, *Six Dynasties Civilization*, New Haven and London, 2007, page 320.

[3] Albert E. Dien, op. cit., page 391.

## 11
## Painted Earthenware Twins
Northern Wei period, early 6th century
Height: 16.3cm

Grey earthenware hollow figural group of twins, standing side by side, holding hands and joined at the forearms and lower bodies. The figures are identically dressed in belted V-necked tunics with billowing sleeves, worn over baggy trousers falling in incised folds beneath which the tips of their shoes emerge. Each twin has a narrow face with delicate features and hair drawn up in double conical buns. The backs of the figures are modelled in low relief. Extensive traces of red and white pigments remain.

Provenance:

J. J. Lally and Co., New York.

Eskenazi Limited, London.

Norman A. Kurland, U. S. A.

Similar examples:

R. L. Hobson, *The George Eumorfopoulos Collection, Catalogue of the Chinese, Corean and Persian Pottery and Porcelain*, volume 6, London, 1928, plate V, F18, for the example now in the Victoria and Albert Museum, London; also, Fujio Koyama, John A. Pope and John Ayers, *Oriental Ceramics, The World's Great Collections*, volume 6, Victoria and Albert Museum, Tokyo, 1976, black and white plate 36.

Nils Palmgren, *Selected Chinese Antiquities from the Collection of Gustaf Adolf, Crown Prince of Sweden*, Stockholm, 1948, plate 67.1; also, Bo Gyllensvärd and John Alexander Pope, *Chinese Art from the Collection of H. M. Gustaf VI Adolf of Sweden*, The Asia Society, New York, 1966, plate 88; also, Mette Siggstedt, *Kinesiska Gravfiguriner*, Stockholm, 1987, page 43, figure 18.

Museum of Fine Arts, Boston, *Exhibition of Chinese Ceramics and of European Drawings*, (Objects in the Exhibition decorate the Home of George de Batz), Boston, 1953, plate 10; also, Christie's, New York, *The Georges de Batz Collection of Chinese Ceramics*, 30 November 1983, number 286.

Annette L. Juliano, *Art of the Six Dynasties, Centuries of Change and Innovation*, New York, 1975, number 19 for the example formerly in the Mr and Mrs Ezekiel Schloss collection; also, Ezekiel Schloss, *Ancient Chinese Ceramic Sculpture from Han through Tang: The Collection of Mr and Mrs Ezekiel Schloss*, volume II, Stamford, Connecticut, 1977, plate 36a.

Osaka Municipal Museum of Art, *Rikucho no bijutsu*, (Arts of the Six Dynasties), Tokyo, 1976, number 133; also, Osaka Municipal Museum of Art, *Rikucho no bijutsu*, (Arts of the Six Dynasties), (Chinese Art Exhibition Series Number 2), Osaka, 1980, page 12, number 1-110.

In many countries, twins exert an especial fascination and, historically and culturally, are revered and reviled in equal measure. In China, they are regarded as an auspicious symbol, a harbinger of good fortune. It seems that this already was the case during the Northern Wei period, given the widely published twin figurines in museum and private collections. Their inclusion in tombs must have been partly due to a general belief in their propitious powers and ability to ward off evil, rather than any specific relevance to the tomb occupants. Such painted earthenware conjoined twin figures seem to be confined to the Northern Wei period and do not appear amongst the tomb figures of the Sui and Tang dynasties. However, in the later periods, the 'Twin Immortals of Happiness and Harmony' (Hehe er xian), represented as a pair of gleeful boys wearing loose clothing, became a popular motif in the decorative arts.

一一

彩绘陶双胞俑

北魏

公元六世纪早期

高 一六·三公分

灰陶胎，空心俑，一组双胞胎，并列站立，牵手靠腿，小臂相依。两俑衣着相同，开领外袍，束腰于中，肥袖宽荡，裤管松垮，垂褶至地，鞋尖显露。双胞脸型狭窄，五官秀美，头发束起，呈双丫髻。俑背浅浮雕塑造。相当面积的红白原色保存完好。

## 12
## Earthenware Model of a Woman at a Well
Northern Wei period, early 6th century
Height: 20.5cm

Grey earthenware model of a woman at a well, her right arm raised, her left held in front, both hands bunched and formed as if to hold a rope attached to a vessel to draw water. She stands with her left foot resting on the edge of the square well head, modelled with projections at its corners, her right foot placed firmly on the circular well. She wears a belted robe with sleeves rolled back to her elbows. Her hair is drawn up into two peaks at the front. A large jar is at her side, resting on the edge of the well, waiting to be filled.

Provenance:

Anthony Hardy, Hong Kong.

Eskenazi Limited, London.

Norman A. Kurland, U. S. A.

Published:

Christie's, New York, *The Hardy Collection of Early Chinese Ceramics and Works of Art from the Sze Yuan Tang*, 21 September 1995, number 57.

Similar example:

R.L. Hobson, *The George Eumorfopoulos Collection, Catalogue of the Chinese, Corean and Persian Pottery and Porcelain*, volume 6, London, 1928, plate IX, number F31.

From the Han period, models of wells were often found as an essential part of tomb furnishings, along with all the other important 'every day' requirements for the afterlife, including stoves, servants, livestock, domestic pets, granaries and so on.[1] Wells were of particular importance to the deceased as they provided a source of water in the afterlife and also represented the gathering point and heart of any village. The rectangular shape of the well head with corner projections is very characteristic of the period and its grid formation lends itself to the form of the written character (*jing*), although circular well heads are also found. Archaeological evidence has shown that many such wells were dug vertically in a circular shape and lined with bricks, after which a circular 'well ring' was sometime added to prevent collapse and then topped by a square stone platform to function as a well head.[2]

The present example is particularly charming as the basic 'function' of the well has been enlivened by the presence of the woman, with arms raised, one leg placed against the well as a counterweight, caught in the action of drawing water to fill her container.

[1] Cary Liu et al., *Recarving China's Past, Art, Archaeology, and Architecture of the "Wu Family Shrines"*, Princeton, 2005, number 18.

[2] Bai Ning, 'Jiankang – The Southern Capital and Metropolitan Life', in Willow Weilan Hai, Annette L. Juliano et al., *Art in a Time of Chaos, Masterworks from Six Dynasties China 3rd - 6th Centuries*, New York, 2016, pages 55 - 56.

一二

灰陶汲水女俑 北魏 公元六世纪早期

高 二０·五公分

灰陶胎，女俑于井边，右臂举起，左手在前，双手握绳，呈提桶取水状。俑为立姿，左脚靠着方形井沿，拟有角架支撑，右脚踏在圆井上。身穿外袍系带，两袖挽至肘部，头发梳成双髻置于前。身边一只大水罐放于井台上，等着盛满。

一三　鎏金銅菩薩立像　北魏　熙平年銘

高二二・○公分

應為公元五一六年

鎏金銅觀音像，高浮雕鑄就，立於圓形蓮台，下承四高足基座。觀音右手施無畏印，左手持淨瓶。此像臉型橢圓，五官精細，發式上梳覆蓋肉髻。身佩胸飾，披帛垂蕩，兩個渦紋顯於肩部，下懸環過臂部，至膝蓋處交叉。衣紋皺褶，流暢而下及腿，各側衣紋形成尖狀，葉形背光，裝點絢麗，周圍火焰紋，鏈環紋鑲邊。觀音腦後頭光，飾以一輪蓮花瓣，背光後面淺浮雕勾勒出精美圖案，包括坐佛居中，兩

## 13
## Gilt-bronze Avalokiteshvara (Guanyin)
Northern Wei period, inscribed with date corresponding to 516
Height: 22.0cm

Gilt-bronze figure of Avalokiteshvara (Guanyin) cast in high relief standing upon a circular lotus petal base, raised on a high four-legged pedestal, with right hand lifted in *abhaya mudra* and left hand holding an ambrosia flask. The deity has an oval face with delicately cast features and his hair is drawn into a high top-knot covering the prominent *ushnisha*. He wears a pectoral and his shawl floats out to two curling points at the shoulders, the ends crossing at the knees and looping over the arms. His garment falls in stylized pleats at the legs and tapers to points to either side. The leaf-shaped mandorla is finely decorated with borders of incised flames and a ring-punched edge; the head of the figure is backed by a halo of radiating lotus petals. The back of the mandorla is cast in low relief with an elaborate scene, comprising a seated Buddha flanked by two attendants above a billowing canopy incised with lotus flowers, enclosing the two seated figures of Shakyamuni and Prabhutaratna beneath. The pedestal is inscribed with a forty-eight-character inscription. The figure is richly gilded.

Provenance:

Hirano Kotoken, Tokyo (Sold by Mr Ryoji Hirano in the 1960s).

Ogawa Sadao collection, Tokyo.

Eskenazi Limited, London.

Norman A. Kurland, U. S. A.

Exhibited:

Osaka, 1976, Osaka Municipal Museum of Art.

Published:

Osaka Municipal Museum of Art, *Rikucho no bijutsu*, (Arts of the Six Dynasties), Tokyo, 1976, number 280.

Osaka Municipal Museum of Art, *Rikucho no bijutsu*, (Arts of the Six Dynasties), (Chinese Art Exhibition Series Number 2), Osaka, 1980, page 33, number 3-144.

Jin Shen, *Zhongguo lidai jinian foxiang tudian*, (Illustrated Chronological Dictionary of Chinese Buddhist Figures), Beijing, 1994, page 141, number 98.

S. Matsubara, *A History of Chinese Buddhist Sculpture*, Tokyo, 1995, plates volume 1, plates 140a and 140b.

Sotheby's, New York, *Fine Chinese Ceramics and Works of Art*, 15 September 2010, number 286.

Similar example:

S. Matsubara, *Chinese Buddhist Sculpture*, Tokyo, 1966, plates 79a, b and c, for a very similar Northern Wei gilt bronze sculpture dated to 519.

侍从随之。莲花饰华盖下，释迦摩尼佛与多宝佛平坐。基座上有铭文四十八字。此像为厚实的鎏金覆盖。

The inscription on the back and sides of the pedestal reads as follows:

熙平元年三月二十三日，清信女佛弟子王贰奴敬造观世音像一躯，上为七世父母，因缘眷属，恒得向佛，闻某正法，所愿如是。

which may be translated as:

On the twenty-third day of the third month of the first year of the Xiping reign [corresponding to 516], the devoted Buddhist disciple Wang Ernu, respectfully commissioned a statue of Guanyin, for all seven generations of the family, for all family members, in order that they might constantly follow the Buddhist teachings, hear the Righteous Way and achieve what they desire.

According to Angela Falco Howard, the standing bodhisattva Guanyin was an 'iconographic innovation of the second half of the fifth century.'[1] The bodhisattva was often depicted with an ambrosia flask in one hand and a lotus in the other. The 'canonical source' for the cult of the Guanyin apparently had its basis in the *Lotus Sutra (Saddharmapundarika Sutra* or *Sutra of the Lotus of the True Dharma)* and the 'compassionate one' was believed to rescue people from a variety of difficulties and dangers. The *Lotus Sutra*, one of the most influential texts of Mahayana Buddhism, may have been translated into Chinese as early as the mid-third century and became increasingly popular by the fifth and sixth centuries.

The seated figures beneath the cusped canopy on the reverse of the present gilt bronze depict the miraculous meeting of the two Buddhas, that of Prabhutaratna, the Buddha of the Past and Shakyamuni, the Buddha of the Present, a key moment in the *Lotus Sutra* and an image that became another iconic innovation of the Northern Wei period. The scene refers to a moment during a sermon by Shakyamuni when a stupa appeared in the sky, containing the relics of Prabhutaratna, because the latter had taken a vow to appear whenever the *Lotus Sutra* was preached. Shakyamuni used his finger as a key, unlocking the door to the stupa to reveal Prabhutaratna. The two Buddhas then seated themselves side by side.

[1] Angela Falco Howard et al., *Chinese Sculpture*, New Haven and London, 2006, pages 250 - 251.

14
## Limestone Stele

Northern Wei period, early 6th century
Height: 45.1cm
Width: 33.6cm
Depth: 9.8cm

Limestone rectangular section of a stele, the top carved with a shallow groove and the base with a tenon. One face is carved with a central canopied niche, in which Buddha is seated, hands in *abhaya* and *varada mudra*, his monk's robes falling in pleats and folds down the front, flanked by a pair of bodhisattvas standing upon lotus bases. To either side are a pair of floating *apsaras* carved in low relief, each above a narrow, arched niche containing a figure of a bodhisattva. Beneath, a pair of donor figures bowing in reverence and a pair of Buddhistic lions, flank a large *boshanlu*. The reverse of the stele is carved with a central, canopied niche containing the seated figure of Maitreya, pendant legs crossed at the ankles, wearing a tall head-dress and dressed in a shawl and *dhoti* which falls over the legs in narrow pleats. To either side are a pair of crouching Buddhist lions and a pair of bodhisattvas holding attributes. The two narrow sides are each carved with a small figure of Buddha seated within a niche, hands held up in *anjali mudra*.

Provenance:

Joseph Chan, Hong Kong, up to 1986.

Sir Joseph Hotung, Hong Kong.

Eskenazi Limited, London.

Frieda and Milton Rosenthal, U. S. A.

Eskenazi Limited, London.

Norman A. Kurland, U. S. A.

Published:

Sotheby's, New York, *Fine Chinese Ceramics and Works of Art including Chinese and Japanese Art from the Collection of Frieda and Milton Rosenthal*, 16 September 2008, number 207.

Similar example:

S. Matsubara, *A History of Chinese Buddhist Sculpture*, Tokyo, 1995, plates volume 1, plate 146a for a larger example, dated to 520, in the Kyoto National Museum.

一四　石灰岩佛龕　北魏　公元六世纪早期

高　四五·一公分　宽　三三·六公分　深　九·八公分

石灰岩，长方形体，或为某雕塑一部，顶刻浅沟纹，底有端块。正面雕中心龕，华盖罩顶，佛陀趺坐，手施以无畏与愿印，身着袈裟，皱褶垂落，集于座前，两旁伴有菩萨立于莲台上。每面都有一对浅浮雕飞天，分刻于两侧窄龕之上，龕中各有菩萨立像。下部刻有一双施主形象，于大型博山炉两边，虔诚鞠躬，佛狮伴随左右。背面主龕中，弥勒佛高坐，悬腿交叉，头戴高饰，身着帔帛兜提，细褶下坠盖腿。两

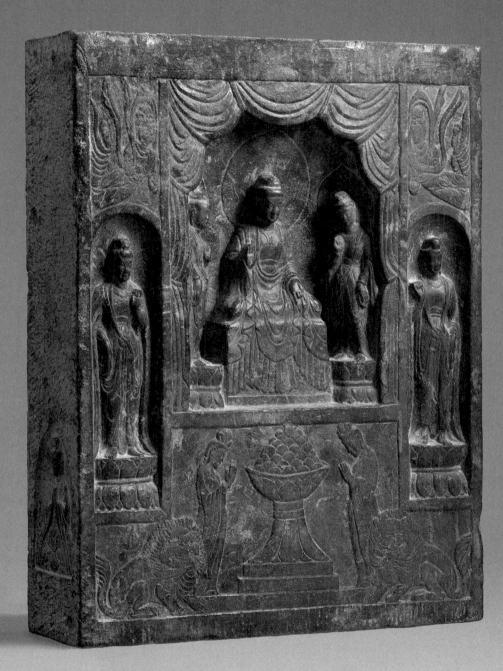

边各有佛狮蜷卧，两尊菩萨均持法器随从。碑侧狭窄，亦刻有小型龛位，内坐佛像，双手合十。

While the main niche on the front of the stele most probably contains a representation of the Buddha Shakyamuni, the historical Buddha, the reverse is carved with Maitreya, the bodhisattva who was supposed to succeed Shakyamuni as the Buddha of the Future. According to Dorothy C. Wong, 'Maitreya's emergence as a cult figure in India around the beginning of the Common Era coincided with important changes within the Buddhist tradition – namely, the developments of the bodhisattva cult and the Mahayana movement.'[1] By the time the worship of Maitreya reached China in the fourth century, it had matured and developed and it became one of the major Buddhist cults, peaking from the end of the fifth century to the first quarter of the sixth. Many depictions, as in the present sculpture, show Maitreya in the Tusita heaven (the fourth of six heavens), waiting to be reborn. Dorothy C. Wong, op. cit., explains that many of the characteristics associated with Maitreya derive from Indian iconography: 'The bodhisattva is depicted with legs crossed at the ankles, a seated position derived from royal portraiture of kings of the Kushan dynasty (late first through third century C. E.); this seated position became identified with Maitreya exclusively. The accompanying lions, a symbol of royalty in India, reinforce Maitreya's stature as a spiritual ruler.'[2]

[1] Dorothy C. Wong, *Chinese Steles, Pre-Buddhist and Buddhist Use of a Symbolic Form*, Honolulu, 2004, page 91.

[2] Dorothy C. Wong, op. cit., page 93.

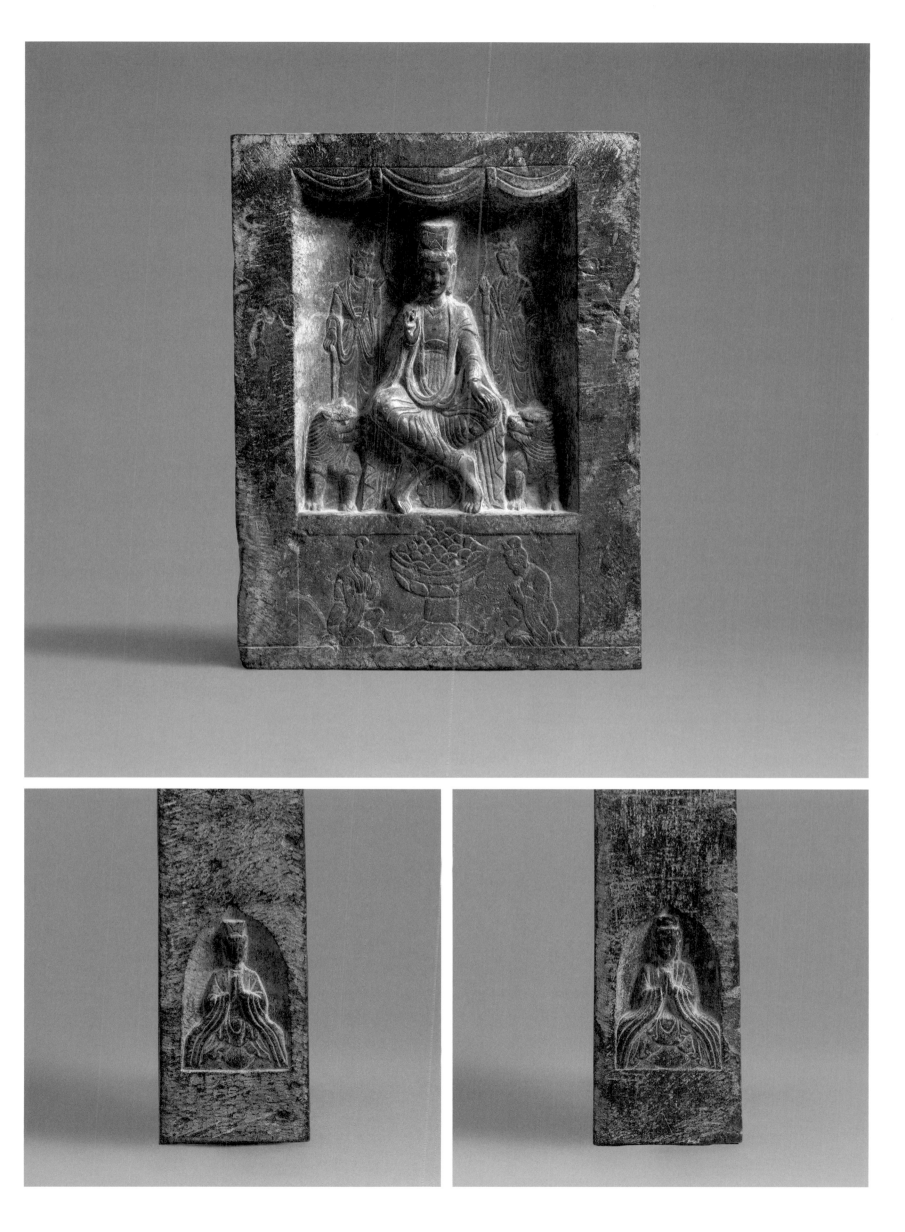

## 15
**Fifteen Painted Earthenware Musicians**
Northern Wei period, early 6th century
Height: c. 13.5 - 13.7cm

Set of fifteen hollow, grey earthenware kneeling female musicians. Each of the slender figures is dressed in a collared, cross-over gown which gathers in an irregular shape around the legs and is secured at the waist by a trailing sash, while two ribbons run down the pleats at the back. The long, flaring sleeves fall wing-like to the back and to the left. Each of the figures has a well-modelled head with refined facial features and a high forehead topped by a small, close-fitting hat, *pingshangze*. The women play a variety of instruments: the zither (*qin*), two types of drum (*gu*), the vertical flute (*xiao*), the horn (*haojiao*), the lute (*pipa*), small cymbals (*xiaobo*), the harp (*konghu*), the panpipes (*paixiao*), small hand-held drums (*shougu*) and one has her hands held up in mid-clap. All the figures bear considerable remains of white, black, red and buff pigments.

Provenance:

J. J. Lally & Co., New York (set of 10); Kaikodo, New York (set of 5).

Norman A. Kurland, U. S. A.

Exhibited:

Princeton, New Jersey, 1998, Princeton University Art Museum.

Similar examples:

Osvald Sirén, *Kinas Konst Under Tre Årtusenden*, volume 1, Stockholm, 1942, page 425, figure 309.

Annette L. Juliano, *Art of the Six Dynasties, Centuries of Change and Innovation*, New York, 1975, number 22 for a set of five musicians wearing *pingshangze*, in the St Louis Art Museum.

Osaka Municipal Museum of Art, *Rikucho no bijutsu*, (Arts of the Six Dynasties), Tokyo, 1976, number 138, for a set of five.

'Luoyang Beiwei Yang Ji mu chutu wenwu', (Cultural Relics from the Northern Wei tomb of Yang Ji, Luoyang), *Wenwu*, volume 11, Beijing, 2007, pages 60 - 61, figures 16 - 23, for a set of eight musicians.

一五 彩绘陶乐俑 北魏 公元六世纪早期

高 一三·五公分 — 一三·七公分

灰陶胎，乐俑空心，此群十五个，均为跪姿女性。身材苗条，穿着右衽长衫，领口宽大，以不规则形散于腿上，腰部宽带系结，两条长缨垂皱背后。长袖外展，如翼在后。每个乐俑面目清秀，五官精致，额头宽展，头戴平上帻。她们演奏多种乐器：琴，两种鼓，箫，号角，琵琶，小钹，箜篌，排箫，手鼓，其一正在鼓掌。所有乐俑均有相当部分的白色，黑色，红色及米黄色存留。

During the Six Dynasties period, music played an important role in court rituals and social gatherings of the elite; in addition, music would have been a key part of funerary ceremonies. Therefore, the presence of earthenware sets of professional musicians in Northern Wei tombs to provide music for the afterlife is unsurprising and such musicians are also found painted on wall murals and carved on stone sarcophagi. The influx of culture and ideas from Central Asia during this time is also evident in the types of instruments being played: 'The typical orchestra underwent significant changes between the Han and the Tang, moving from an emphasis on clamorous percussion instruments to a lighter sound produced by a mixture of strings, wind instruments, and small drums.'[1] The present group of musicians is remarkable for the range of instruments they play and the combination of wind, string and percussion seen here coincides with the shift described above. The instruments vary from the more traditional, such as the zither (*qin*), to the lute (*pipa*), which is thought to have been a later arrival. The dissemination of Buddhism during this period was also a factor in changing musical tastes: 'Music played an important part in Buddhist chants, and depiction of the Buddhist paradises included representation of music and dance. Acceptance of these new musical forms was facilitated by the growing popularity of Buddhism itself.'[2] The rise in popularity of the *konghou* or harp during this time is also thought to be due to its prominent role in Buddhist music.

[1] Albert E. Dien, *Six Dynasties Civilization*, New Haven and London, 2007, page 339.

[2] Albert E. Dien, op. cit., page 343.

16
**Limestone Maitreya**
Northern Wei period, first quarter of the 6th century
Longmen cave temples, Henan province.
Height: 52.5cm

Grey limestone figure of Maitreya, seated cross-legged in *virasana* with right foot on left leg, his hands in *abhaya* and *varada mudra*. The deity has a long, narrow head with strongly carved features: arching brows over eyes half-closed in contemplation, broad nose and bud-like mouth. His hair is neatly arranged over the prominent *ushnisha*, leaving the pendulous ears visible. He wears long-sleeved, flowing robes which fall in pleats and folds over the arms and to the front, leaving his right foot visible, with a knotted sash around his neck. The sculpture is partly covered in a beige-coloured layer, probably the base for the colours which once decorated it, now calcified on the surface of the dark grey stone. The back is unworked.

Provenance:

Longmen cave temples, Henan province.

L. Wannieck, Paris.

M.D.-A.V., Brussels.

Eskenazi Limited, London.

Norman A. Kurland, U. S. A.

Exhibited:

Gent, 1979, Centrum voor Kunst en Cultuur.

Princeton, New Jersey, 1999, Princeton University Art Museum.

Published:

N. De Bisscop, *China, Cultur Vroeger en Nu*, Gent, 1979, number 288.

Sun Di, *Comprehensive Illustrated Catalogue of Chinese Buddhist Statues in Overseas Collections*, volume 1, Beijing, 2005, page 167.

Similar examples:

S. Mizuno and T. Nagahiro, *A Study of the Buddhist Cave-Temples at Lung-Mên, Ho-nan*, Tokyo, 1941, plate 39, for a figure in a niche in the lower section of the north wall of the Lianhua Cave, inscribed below with a date corresponding to 527; also, *Longmen Shiku*, (Longmen Caves), Beijing, 1961, plate 51; also, Wen Yucheng ed., *Zhongguo meishu quanji, diaosu bian 11, Longmen shiku diaoke*, (The Great Treasury of Chinese Art, Sculpture 11, Longmen Caves), Shanghai, 1988, page 62, plate 63.

*Longmen Shiku*, (Longmen Caves), Beijing, 1961, plate 20, for a similar figure in a niche carved into the north-west section in the Guyang Cave.

René-Yvon Lefebvre d'Argencé ed., *Chinese, Korean and Japanese Sculpture in the Avery Brundage Collection*, San Francisco, 1974, plate 30; also, Stanley K. Abe, *Ordinary Images*, Chicago, 2002, page 242, figure 4.61.

Wen Yucheng ed., *Zhongguo meishu quanji, diaosu bian 11, Longmen shiku diaoke*, (The Great Treasury of Chinese Art, Sculpture 11, Longmen Caves), Shanghai, 1988, page 48, plate 49; also, Jan van Alphen ed., *The Buddha in the Dragon Gate*, Gent, 2001, number 1 and front cover for a figure of Buddha originally situated in the Guyang Cave.

一六　石灰岩弥勒坐像

龙门石窟　河南　北魏　公元六世纪早期之前半期

高　五二・五公分

石灰岩，弥勒佛双腿交叉，结跏趺坐，右脚放于左腿之上，双手施无畏与愿印。神祇长脸窄面，雕刻鲜明，眉毛弯拱，两眼半闭，呈思维态，宽鼻撅嘴。头式整齐，复盖高肉髻，长耳垂肩。身穿长袖袍，飘逸垂落，皱褶过臂趋前，右脚显露，披帛环颈系结。此像部分覆盖以米色层，应为当年装饰的底色，如今钙化于表面。像背不曾雕琢。

The Buddhist cave temples of Longmen partly owe their magnificence to the patronage of the Tuoba imperial dynasty, the foreign rulers of Northern China from 386 to 535. The emperor Wencheng (440 - 465) initiated the construction of the Buddhist cave temples of Yungang, close to his capital city Pingcheng (later Datong) in northern Shanxi, in remorseful response to the Buddhist persecutions of the previous ruler, his grandfather the emperor Taiwu (408 - 452). In 493, the emperor Xiaowen moved the capital away from the northern border area to the more centrally situated and indigenously Chinese city of Luoyang. This was in pursuit of his sinicization of the dynasty, resulting in expansion to the construction at nearby Longmen that had already been initiated before the move.[1]

The sculpting of cave temples was to continue at Longmen for several hundred years, the greatest number worked during the Tang period (618 - 907). The main caves carved under the Northern Wei, in the forty years before the collapse of the dynasty in 535, include the Central Binyang cave, conceived and partly executed under direct imperial patronage, and the more variously supported Lianhua, Weizi and Guyang caves, the latter 'not a product of imperial patronage, although several royal patrons and high officials sponsored the making of many images within the wall niches.'[2] Indeed, in distinct contrast to Yungang, it is the proliferation of inscriptions at Longmen that makes these caves important historical documents as well as embodiments of religious art of a high order.

Although a subsidiary figure, and one of several such, the sculpture in the present exhibition probably occupied its own niche, the incline of the head suggesting that it may have been placed on a wall curving inwards towards the ceiling. With its strict frontality, elongated proportions and cascade of overlapping, folded drapery obscuring most of the body beneath, it is an exemplar of Northern Wei Longmen style.

[1] Jan van Alphen ed., *The Buddha in the Dragon Gate*, Gent, 2001, page 41.

[2] Angela Falco Howard et al., *Chinese Sculpture*, New Haven and London, 2006, page 240.

17
**Pair of Painted Earthenware Figures**
Northern Wei period, early 6th century
Height: 32.4cm and 32.5cm

Pair of grey earthenware figures, probably civil officials, each standing with head slightly inclined, right arm raised to the waist and left pendant, the hands hidden. Each of the elongated, finely modelled figures is wearing *liangdang* armour - a breast- and back-plate connected by straps over the shoulders and fastened with cords at the waist - on top of court clothing: a short tunic with voluminous sleeves over baggy trousers tied below the knee. Each has a small head, fashioned with delicate features – narrowed eyes, small nose and mouth and high forehead surmounted by a small, close-fitting hat, *pingshangze*. The back of each of the figures is flat with some incised details. The figures bear the remains of red, black and white pigments.

Provenance:

Kaikodo, New York.

Norman A. Kurland, U. S. A.

Exhibited:

New York, 1997, Kaikodo.

Princeton, New Jersey, 1997, Princeton University Art Museum.

Published:

Kaikodo, *Kaikodo Journal*, New York, 1997, number 35.

Similar examples:

Jean-Pierre Dubosc, *Mostra d'Arte Cinese*, (Exhibition of Chinese Art), Venice, 1954, number 305.

George Kuwayama et al., *The Joy of Collecting, Far Eastern Art from the Lidow Collection*, Los Angeles, 1979, number 34.

Candace J. Lewis, *Into the Afterlife: Han and Six Dynasties Tomb Sculpture from the Schloss Collection*, New York, 1990, number 44.

Ellen B. Avril, *Chinese Art in the Cincinnati Art Museum*, Cincinnati, 1997, page 140, number 52.

For a discussion of *liangdang* armour and the garment worn beneath it, refer to the footnote to catalogue number 10.

一七　彩绘陶士人俑一对　北魏　公元六世纪早期

高　三二·四公分
　　三二·五公分

灰陶胎，一对站姿士人俑，头微前敛，右臂抬至腰际，左臂下垂，藏手袖中。陶俑制作精良，体型略长，身披两挡甲，胸背各一片，宽带上接，跨肩而佩，下系带于腰间。俑头较小，五官精巧，纤细双目，口鼻小巧，前额高起，戴平上帻。俑背平坦，少许刻纹。俑身保存红黑色及白色。

## 18

# Painted Earthenware Walking Ox
*Northern Wei period, early 6th century*
Length: 19.5cm

Grey earthenware hollow ox standing on a trapezoid base, its right foreleg raised as if walking while ploughing. The animal is delicately modelled with typical pronounced dewlap, cloven hooves, pointed horns and projecting ears. Its head, with bulging eyes and curled nostrils, is marked with folds of flesh and bound by a halter composed of straps and roundels. There are traces of red pigment on ears and hooves and white on the base.

Provenance:

Eskenazi Limited, London.

Norman A. Kurland, U. S. A.

Similar examples:

Matsuoka Museum of Art, *Inaugural Exhibiiton, Selected Masterpieces of the Matsuoka Museum of Art*, Tokyo, 1975, number 17 for an animal standing four-square on its base.

*Sekai toji zenshu*, (Ceramic Art of the World), Chinese Prehistoric and Ancient Periods, volume 10, Tokyo, 1982, page 253, plate 275 for another example standing four-square.

For a discussion of the ox and its representation during the Six Dynasties period, refer to the footnote to catalogue number 38.

一八　彩绘陶耕牛　北魏　公元六世纪早期

长一九・五公分

灰陶胎，牛体内空，立于梯形座上。右前腿抬起，犹如耕地前行。此牛塑造精细，典型的赘肉，偶蹄尖角，两耳竖直。牛头上暴目突睛，鼻吻曲软，肉褶明显，佩戴笼头，条带固定，上饰圆扣。蹄子耳朵处有红彩痕迹，底座也有白色遗留。

19

## Pair of Painted Earthenware Earth Spirits

Northern Wei period, early 6th century
Height: 26.0cm and 26.5cm

Pair of grey earthenware hollow earth spirits, seated on their haunches on shaped bases. The slightly smaller figure is modelled as a lion-like creature with upright ears, open mouth, snarling muzzle, sharp teeth and lolling tongue. Its mane falls to either side of its chest above furled wings with scrolling tips. Its tail curls up against its rump below a row of three flat, curved spikes projecting from its spine and head. The companion figure has a humanoid face with bulging eyes, lumpen nose, downturned mouth, fringed beard and head rising to a point, but is otherwise similar. Both earth spirits are painted, with much red pigment along the spines and on the haunches.

Provenance:

Chang Wei-hwa, Taibei, Taiwan.

Norman A. Kurland, U. S. A.

Exhibited:

Princeton, New Jersey, 1998, Princeton University Art Museum.

Similar examples:

Luoyang Museum, 'The Northern Wei Tomb cf Yuan Shao at Loyang', *Kaogu*, volume 4, Beijing, 1973, plate 12, figures 1 and 2, for a pair of earth spirits from the tomb of Yuan Shao; also, Lin Shuzhong ed., *Zhongguo meishu quanji, diaosu bian 3, Wei Jin nanbeichao diaosu*, (The Great Treasury of Chinese Art, Sculpture 3, Six Dynasties), Beijing, 1988, page 134, plate 112, for one of the pair.

Such seated earth spirits or tomb guardians – *zhenmushou* – were found in pairs, usually one with an animal face and the other with a human one, from the early sixth century, their grotesque and fearsome features intended to subdue evil spirits and provide protection. Recorded examples include the pair, cited above, that are part of a set of 115 processional figures found in the tomb of Prince Yuan Shao (d. 528) and his wife (d. 520), now in the Luoyang Museum.[1]

[1] Robert D. Jacobsen, *Celestial Horses and Long Sleeve Dancers, The David W. Dewey Collection of Ancient Chinese Tomb Sculpture*, Minneapolis, 2013, pages 133 - 134.

一九　彩绘陶镇墓兽一对　北魏　公元六世纪早期

高　二六·〇公分　二六·五公分

陶胎，镇墓兽内空，蜷坐于后腿，下垫底座。略小型者，塑以狮面，耳朵竖起，口张嘴咧，凶猛咆哮，利齿尖牙，长舌外挂。鬃毛贴胸两侧，羽翼丰满，端部内卷。尾巴弯曲靠住后臀，头和脊椎上，三根扁平弯角挺立。另一兽身人面，目凸鼻涕，嘴角下咧，络腮胡须，鬃毛贴头微上扬，其余与同伴相似。两神兽均施彩绘，沿着脊椎及后腿以红色为主。

## 20
## Painted Earthenware Camel
Northern Wei period, early 6th century
Height: 23.5cm

Grey earthenware two-humped, Bactrian camel, the hollow animal standing four-square on a rectangular base. The finely modelled camel stands on its two-toed feet with head held high, its eyes, ears, nostrils, teeth and muzzle sharply delineated, with a long strip of hair running from its chin to its chest. It bears a heavy load slung between its humps over slatted boards, including a long roll of bedding, two hares, two flasks, a twisted skein of material, probably silk, and a saddle bag with slit opening on top. The figure bears traces of red, white and pink pigments.

### Provenance:

Rasmussen, Copenhagen, April 1960.

L. F. Foght, Copenhagen.[1]

Private collection.

Eskenazi Limited, London.

Norman A. Kurland, U. S. A.

### Exhibited:

Copenhagen, 1950, Kunstindustrimuseet, (Danish Museum of Art and Design).

### Published:

André Leth, *Kinas Kunst i Svensk og Dansk Eje*, (Chinese Art in Swedish and Danish Collections), Copenhagen, 1950, number 245.

Arne Bruun Rasmussen, *The Louis Foght Collections*, auction catalogue, Copenhagen, 4 - 8 April 1960, number 897.

Christie's, London, *Fine Chinese Ceramics, Jades and Works of Art*, 12 June 1989, number 124A.

### Similar examples:

René-Yvon Lefebvre d'Argencé, *Chinese Ceramics in the Avery Brundage Collection*, San Francisco, 1967, plate XVIA.

Luoyang Museum, 'The Northern Wei Tomb of Yuan Shao at Loyang', *Kaogu*, volume 4, Beijing, 1973, page 221, number 7.

Robert D. Jacobsen, *Celestial Horses and Long Sleeve Dancers, The David W. Dewey Collection of Ancient Chinese Tomb Sculpture*, Minneapolis, 2013, pages 133 - 134.

[1] The following information has been kindly supplied by Jesper Bruun Rasmussen:
Louis Foght was a Copenhagen dealer, mainly in rugs and textiles, and a serious collector of eighteenth and nineteenth century Danish paintings, eighteenth century furniture, eighteenth century Danish silver and a wide range of oriental art. After his death, his collection was sold over four days in 1960 by the auctioneers, Rasmussen.

二〇

彩绘陶骆驼　北魏　公元六世纪早期

高 二三・五公分

灰陶胎，双峰驼，空心塑造，立于方形底座上。骆驼形象逼真，脚分两趾，头高扬起，眼睛，耳朵，鼻吻，牙齿及口唇，均精雕细琢，长缕鬃毛从颔下至前胸。驼峰之间条板斜架，承负重载，包括行李一卷，野兔两只，扁壶一对，绞扭物件或为丝绸，还有顶盖打开的鞍袋。此像表面存有红色白色及粉色的痕迹。

The camel provides a wonderful metaphor for the cultural exchange between China and Central Asia during this period and Northern Wei examples such as the present one are the precursors of the more well-known glazed Tang versions. The land routes established during the Han period (206 BC - 220 AD) continued to thrive and the load on this camel reflects the transient life of a merchant or traveller on the Silk Route, including the rolls of bedding, possibly made of felt, twists of material to be traded, together with provisions for the journey, including the pilgrim flask of wine, food in the form of the dead rabbits and the saddle bag containing further supplies. The slatted pack board may have doubled up as the collapsible lattice walls of a yurt, as suggested by Elfriede Regina Knauer, *The Camel's Load in Life and Death*, Zurich, 1998, pages 48 - 49.

## 21
## Limestone Panel

Northern Wei period, first quarter of the sixth century
Gongxian cave temples, Henan province
Length: 43.7cm
Height: 24.0cm

Grey limestone panel, a fragment from a carved frieze, depicting a procession of six female figures. The main figure in the group, probably an aristocratic donor, is depicted on a larger scale with more space around her, indicating her significance and status. She stands with her right arm outstretched and palm flexed, while the left hand holds a lotus-shaped offering bowl to her waist. Her head is shown in three-quarter profile and her rounded face is finely carved with arched brows, elongated, downcast eyes and small mouth set in a pensive smile. Her hair is neatly drawn up in a double chignon revealing the high forehead. She is accompanied by five smaller figures, probably attendants, one to her left and four to her right, arranged in an overlapping row, one holding a bowl, another with hands clasped inside her sleeves. Their oval faces are carved with arched eyebrows and narrowed eyes, and their mouths with a half-smiling, gentle expression. The attendants are differentiated by their hairstyles - some have double top-knots, others have single buns. All the women wear wide-sleeved loose robes, the lapels forming a V-shape at the front and, in some cases, fastened with a wide sash at the chest. Behind the figures are the handle of a large fan, the upper part of which is missing, and a dangling tassel, probably from a parasol, originally above the main figure. Traces of red, blue and yellowish pigment remain on the dark grey stone. The back of the stone is unworked.

Provenance:

Gongxian cave temples, Henan province, Cave 1, south-west corner.

Hashimoto Kansetsu, Kyoto.

Eskenazi Limited, London.

Dr and Mrs Hans König, Minusio, Switzerland.

Eskenazi Limited, London.

Norman A. Kurland, U. S. A.

Exhibited:

Nagoya, 1958, Aichi Prefectural Museum of Art.

Osaka, 1966, Osaka Municipal Museum of Art.

Osaka, 1976, Osaka Municipal Museum of Art.

Osaka, 1995, Osaka Municipal Museum of Art.

New York, March 2002, Eskenazi Limited at PaceWildenstein.

二一　石灰岩礼佛像　北魏　公元六世纪早期之前半期

巩县石窟　河南　长　四三·七公分　高　二四·0公分

石灰岩，此像为大型雕塑一部，刻划了六名女士，中心者应为一位贵族施主，其形象大于她人，显示出她的尊贵和地位。她右臂前伸展掌，左手持莲钵于腰。头部圆脸微侧，弯眉细目，眼帘低垂，小嘴笑意。她的发梳向上，呈双髻于宽额前。五位侍女随从，一左四右，一行均为椭圆脸，弯眉细眼，嘴露笑容，温文尔雅。仕女头式各异，有双高髻，也有单髻。女士均穿宽袖松袍，翻一位持碗，另一袖手。

Processions of devotees worshipping the Buddha appear to have been popularized during the second half of the Northern Wei period and are to be found at the Longmen and Gongxian cave temples amongst others. At Gongxian, Caves 1, 3 and 4 are decorated with friezes of devotees on the interior, flanking the entrance; the first two caves have three tiers of carvings on each side of the entrance, but Cave 4 has four incomplete tiers. Of all the Gongxian caves, the processional carvings in Cave 1 are apparently both the most complete and of the highest quality. The top and largest tiers represent the emperor (on the south-east wall) and the empress (on the south-western wall), each with entourage and attendants. Below the emperor are two panels representing male aristocrats and their attendants forming an impressive procession, while on the opposite side are the female aristocrats and their attendants, carved in two panels beneath the empress.[1] It would appear that the original location for the present fragment was at the back of the second tier, below the empress.[2]

Artistically these friezes display great virtuosity both in their sculptural and compositional qualities, employing high, low and medium relief carving to give a sense of perspective and depth. The second tier on the south-west wall of Cave 1 demonstrates this well. The whole panel is framed on either side by a tree, while a Buddhist nun leads at the front of the procession, holding an incense burner. The scene is further divided into 'cells' which move the eye along in a rhythmic way. There are four main figures, their status shown by their greater size, of which the larger figure in the present fragment is one; each is followed by four smaller attendants. The groups are separated in each case by a large canopy or umbrella over the main figure and an oval fan behind her. As has been pointed out by Ann Paludan, the carving has been created with a 'meticulous attention to angle of viewing. The scenes would have been seen by the right or left by those entering the cave to worship. The edges of the robes and noses of the figures are therefore deliberately accentuated, projecting to the right or left to make the correct impression on the viewer in the centre.'[3] It is possible that such friezes were based on paintings, now lost, as has been suggested in the case of some of the processional scenes at Longmen.[4]

These friezes are remarkable also for their social significance. It appears that the works at Gongxian started around 517, the second year that Lady Hu (consort to Emperor Xuanwu) assumed the regency as Dowager Ling. She ruled as regent for her son from 515 - 520 and again from 525 - 528 and was a major patron of Buddhism. It is probable that Caves 1 and 2 were built for Xuanwu (posthumously) and Lady Hu, and that the imperial donors carved on the south wall in Cave 1 may be portrayals of them.[5] In addition, the friezes represent a cross-section of sixth century Northern Wei court society and within the processional groups are seen a wide range in age and sex, all represented with a high degree of individuality.

[1] Chen Mingda, ed., *Zhongguo meishu quanji; diaosubian 13: Gongxian, Tianlongshan, Xiangtangshan, Anyang shiku diaoke*, (A Treasury of Chinese Art; Sculpture, volume 13: Gongxian, Tianlongshan, Xiangtangshan, Anyang - Cave Sculptures), Beijing, 1989, pages 11, 12 and 13, and numbers 40 - 60. See also, T. Akiyama and S. Matsubara, *Arts of China; Buddhist Cave Temples, New Researches* Tokyo, 1969, page 231 for a line drawing of the southern wall in Cave 1.

[2] Osaka Municipal Museum of Art, *Chinese Buddhist Stone Sculpture: Veneration of the Sublime*, Osaka, 1995, page 42, number 18.

[3] Ann Paludan, *Chinese Sculpture, A Great Tradition*, Chicago, 2006, pages 215 - 216.

[4] Jan van Alphen ed., *The Buddha at the Dragon Gate*, Gent, 2001, pages 76 - 78. See Angela Falco Howard et al., *Chinese Sculpture*, New Haven and London, 2006, pages 240 - 241 for two processional panels from Longmen, one now in the Metropolitan Museum of Art and the other in the Nelson-Atkins Museum of Art.

[5] See D. Wong, 'Women as Buddhist Art Patrons during the Northern and Southern Dynasties', in Wu Hung ed., *Between Han and Tang: Religious Art and Archaeology in a Transformative Period*, Beijing, 2000, page 545.

二二　彩绘陶佩甲马　北魏　公元六世纪早期

高　二六·0公分

灰陶胎，马腹内空，立于长方形底座上。塑造精细，部分佩甲，马头除了口吻和鼻子，余部面罩覆盖，眼部留出圆孔，结带于竖耳后固定。面罩竖线清晰，以示甲片，点纹饰线应仿饰钉而做。马前甲胄保护，直至胸下，从遗留的彩色甲片饰纹，显现曾具有的功能。此马驮负塞满的鞍袋，袋口敞开，置鞍鞯之上。鞯带三段组成，经尾下过，尾扁平且略弯。此像有红色黑色和白色迹遗留。

## 22
## Painted Earthenware Horse
Northern Wei period, early 6th century
Height: 26.0cm

Grey earthenware horse, the hollow animal standing four-square on a rectangular base. The finely modelled horse is partly armoured. Its head is concealed, apart from the mouth and nostrils, by a crested chanfron with circular openings for the eyes, secured by a strap running behind the upright ears. The structure of the chanfron is clearly marked by vertical lines to represent the plates of armour and by columns of pinpricks, probably imitating studs, that may have once been filled. The front of the horse is protected by armour, hanging to just below the chest, that still bears traces of the painted lamellar decoration that would once have made its function clear. The animal carries a bulging saddle bag with slit opening on top, placed over a saddle cloth. A crupper strap composed of three joined strips runs under the slightly curved, flat tail. The figure bears traces of red, black and white pigments.

Provenance:

Eskenazi Limited, London.

Neil F. Phillips Q. C., Montreal and Virginia.

Eskenazi Limited, London.

Norman A. Kurland, U. S. A.

Exhibited:

Los Angeles, 1997-8, Los Angeles County Museum of Art.

Similar examples:

Annette L. Juliano, *Art of the Six Dynasties, Centuries of Change and Innovation*, New York, 1975, number 31, for a horse wearing full armour and with rider; and number 36, for a pack horse without armour in the Asian Art Museum of San Francisco.

Although there is some literary indication of its earlier adoption, physical evidence for horse armour proper (or bardings) in China is only found towards the end of the Han period.[1] As has been explained by Albert E. Dien, the appearance of the stirrup, around the fourth century in China, led to the full-scale adoption of horse armour:

> 'The appearance of the stirrup, probably in the fourth century, made possible heavier armor. The same dangers to which the rider's armor was a response, as well as the expense of the warrior's equipment, then made the development of armor for the horse worthwhile.'[2]

The painted detail on the chest guard and chanfron of the present figure indicates that the horse is wearing 'lamellar' armour characteristic of the Six Dynasties period. The armour comprises plates or lamellae – either of lacquered leather, steel or iron – pierced at the corners with holes for attachment in overlapping rows. The discovery of 180 pieces of lamellae of different sizes in the Northern Yan tomb of Feng Sufu in Beipiao, Liaoning province, was an unusually rich find.[3] For a line drawing of an actual chanfron unearthed from a tomb at Ershitaixiang, Chaoyang, Liaoning, see Albert E. Dien, 'Armor in China before the Tang Dynasty', *Journal of East Asian Archaeology*, volume 2, issue 3, Leiden, 2000, page 43, figure 19.

[1] Albert E. Dien, 'A Study of Early Chinese Armor', *Artibus Asiae*, volume XLIII, 1/2, Ascona, 1981 - 2, pages 36 - 41.

[2] Albert E. Dien, op. cit., page 36.

[3] 'Liaoning Beipiaoxian Xiguanyingzi Beiyan Feng Sufu mu', (The Northern Yan Tomb of Feng Sufu, Xiguanyingzi, Beipiao county, Liaoning province), *Wenwu*, volume 3, Beijing, 1973, page 28, figures 52 - 58; see also Albert E. Dien, *Six Dynasties Civilization*, New Haven and London, 2007, page 332, figure 10.1.

二三　彩绘陶马　北魏　公元六世纪早期

高　二四·〇公分

灰陶胎，空心马，立于长方形底座上。此马头型长且窄，吻部弯曲，鼻翼外张，长眼睫毛，辔头上系带结绳，饰以扣钉，大圆挂件饰于额前。周身装饰，头顶流苏点缀，弯颈饰有镶板，边缘起伏，或是模仿皮甲，板面圆形花蕾纹，缠枝纹边。胸前带悬挂一组梨形花纹饰件，辔带上印有圆饰纹，向后过臀，经马尾下绕回。鞍子的梯形障泥外展，毛毯覆盖垂下，端部绞状。障泥上印兽纹，面面相对，每只口含花卉，边沿饰以缠枝蔓纹。辔带挂于臀，上悬饰牌。马身部分依旧留有红色，极少量的蓝色。

23
**Painted Earthenware Horse**
Northern Wei period, early 6th century
Height: 24.0cm

Grey earthenware hollow horse, standing four-square on a rectangular base. The horse is modelled with an elongated, narrow head with curved muzzle, flared nostrils and long eyelashes and wears a bridle composed of straps, cords and buckles or studs, a large roundel hanging against its forehead. The animal is elsewhere laden with decorative trappings: a tasselled strip rests over the top of its head and, over the arched neck, are panels with wavy borders, probably imitating leather armour, impressed with roundels forming flowerheads and edged with scrolls. The breast strap is hung with flower-decorated pear-shaped pendants and the crupper strap, impressed with roundels, runs over the rump and under the tail. The saddle has projecting trapezoid flaps to the side, over all of which has been thrown a fringed cloth with twisted ends. The flaps are impressed with designs of confronted felines each holding a flower in its mouth, all edged with scrolling tendrils. The crupper strap is hung, at the haunches, with panels decorated with vases holding, perhaps, stylised branches. The figure still bears areas of red pigment with very small traces of blue.

Provenance:

Eskenazi Limited, London.

Norman A. Kurland, U. S. A.

Exhibited:

Princeton, New Jersey, 1997, Princeton University Art Museum.

Los Angeles, 1997 - 8, Los Angeles County Museum of Art.

Published:

Giuseppe Eskenazi in collaboration with Hajni Elias, *A Dealer's Hand, The Chinese Art Market Through the Eyes of Giuseppe Eskenazi*, London, 2012, page 254, plate 203.

Similar examples:

Royal Ontario Museum, *Chinese Pottery Figurines*, Toronto, 1950, number 3, for a very similar horse apparently unearthed in Luoyang from the tomb of Prince Zhenxing, who died in 525; also, Michael Sullivan, *The Arts of China*, Berkeley and Los Angeles, 1973, page 119, plate 93.

Annette L. Juliano, *Art of the Six Dynasties: Centuries of Change and Innovation*, New York, 1975, catalogue number 34, also illustrated on cover; also, Ezekiel Schloss, *Ancient Chinese Ceramic Sculpture from Han through T'ang*, Stamford, Connecticut, 1977, colour plate III.

Cleveland Museum of Art, *Handbook*, Cleveland, 1978, page 329, number 29.985; also, Cleveland Museum of Art, *Handbook*, Cleveland, 1991, page 19.

Osaka Municipal Museum of Art, *Rikucho no bijutsu*, (Arts of the Six Dynasties), Tokyo, 1976, number 142; also, Tenri University Sankokan Museum, *Tenri hizo meihin-ten* (Exhibition of Masterworks from the Tenri Museum), Osaka, 1992, page 100, plate 332.

This beautifully modelled horse is a classic example of the elegant, attenuated Northern Wei style, visible across the arts from Buddhist sculpture to earthenware figures, which became apparent after the move of the capital to Luoyang in the early sixth century.[1] The slender arching neck and graceful proportions of the animal are complemented by the finely impressed and extraordinarily detailed designs of abstract patterns, felines and vases on the trappings. The high regard in which horses were held during this period is evident in this finely modelled caparisoned example. It has been suggested that such earthenware riderless caparisoned horses symbolized the movement of the deceased to another realm.[2]

[1] For further discussion of this stylistic change, refer to the essay 'Northern Dynasties (386 - 581): Sculpture in Turbulent Times' by Annette L. Juliano, pages 23 - 24 in the present catalogue.

[2] Susan L. Beningson, 'Negotiating the Afterlife in Tombs of the Northern and Southern Dynasties', in Willow Weilan Hai, Annette L. Juliano et al., *Art in a Time of Chaos, Masterworks from Six Dynasties China 3rd - 6th Centuries*, New York, 2016, page 130.

## 24
**Painted Earthenware Attendant or Civil Official**
Western Wei period, 535 - 557
Height: 40.0cm

Grey earthenware male attendant or civil official modelled in the round, standing on a rectangular base, legs slightly apart, hands placed above one another at his chest. He wears a shawl-collared jacket, bordered at top and bottom, crossing to the right, with voluminous, long sleeves that conceal his hands, over flared trousers. His hair is dressed in a most unusual fashion with a small bun on top and arranged into a flat triangular shape at the back. The figure bears considerable areas of white slip and red and black pigment on, respectively, the trousers, jacket and back of the head, where it delineates the hair.

Provenance:

Beurdeley & cie, Paris.

Norman A. Kurland, U. S. A.

Exhibited:

Paris, 1991, Beurdeley & cie.

Published:

Beurdeley & cie, *Art de la Chine*, Paris, 1991, number 12.

Similar example:

The Municipal Museum of Hanzong, 'Excavations of the Tombs of the Western Wei Dynasty (535 - 556) at Cuijiaying near Hanzhong,' *Kaogu yu Wenwu*, volume 2, Xi'an, 1981, plate 10, figures 4 and 5 for a Western Wei figure excavated at Cuijiaying, Hanzhong, Shaanxi province, now in the National Museum of China; also, Shi Yan, *Zhongguo diaosushi tulu 2*, (Catalogue of Chinese Sculpture 2), Shanghai, 1987, page 471, figure 548; also, Susan L. Caroselli ed., *The Quest for Eternity, Chinese Ceramic Sculptures from the People's Republic of China*, Los Angeles, 1987, catalogue number 53, pages 80 and 125 - 126; also, James C. Y. Watt, *China, Dawn of a Golden Age, 200 - 750 AD*, New York, 2004, number 119.

It has been suggested that figures such as the present one represent individuals from the south of China, part of a group of southerners, generically termed 'Man', living in areas of present-day Shaanxi, northern Hubei and south-eastern Sichuan, who were under the jurisdiction of the Southern Dynasties and allied with the south.[1] They were said to have retained their own characteristic dress and manner of hairstyle – a type of pointed bun (*tuiji*) as seen on the present figure, as well as other distinctive cultural features. The closely related example cited above now in the National Museum of China, was excavated in Cuijiayang, Hanzhong, Shaanxi province, along with over seventy other grey earthenware figures of civil and military officials and soldiers.[2]

[1] James C. Y. Watt, *China, Dawn of a Golden Age, 200 - 750 AD*, New York, 2004, number 119.

[2] The Municipal Museum of Hanzong, 'Excavations of the Tombs of the Western Wei Dynasty (535 - 556) at Cuijiaying near Hanzhong,' *Kaogu yu Wenwu*, volume 2, Xi'an, 1981, where it is suggested that the figure may be of the Shu minority group from Sichuan.

二四　彩绘陶侍者或官员俑

高　四〇·〇公分

西魏　公元五三五年—五五七年

灰陶胎，男侍从或官员俑，塑形丰满，站于长方形基座上，双腿略分，双手相叠，置于胸前。身穿宽领外衣，上下镶边，左衽宽袂，长袖罩手，下着长裤，裤腿宽松外展。发式罕见，小鬏为顶，平面三角为尾，称为魋髻。此俑相当部分敷白浆，之后分别在裤子外衣和后脑发际处，加施红黑两色。

## 25

## Red Sandstone Buddhist Votive Stele
Northern Wei period, inscribed with date corresponding to 520
Height: 30.5cm

Red sandstone rectangular votive stele in the form of a two-storey pagoda, each storey topped by a sloping, ridged roof and supported on a low rectangular platform incised with a foliate scroll on one long side and striding, sinuous dragons on the shorter sides. The front of the lower storey is carved in medium relief with a shallow niche containing the figure of Buddha, seated in *virasana* on a low dais with hands in *abhaya mudra*, wearing a monastic robe open at the chest which falls in narrow pleats down his body, his head backed by a large halo with radiating lines. Flanking the central image are three niches on either side, each containing a meditating Buddha. The upper storey is carved with a pair of seated Buddhas, probably Prabhutaratna and Shakyamuni, within an arched niche. The narrow sides are each carved below with a single niche, one with a standing figure of Buddha with hands clasped together in *anjali mudra* and the other with the figure of Maitreya with legs crossed at the ankles, while a single phoenix is shown in the upper storey above each figure. The reverse is carved on both storeys with a thirty-three-character inscription in all.

Provenance:

J. J. Lally & Co., New York.

Norman A. Kurland, U. S. A.

Similar examples:

S. Matsubara, *A History of Chinese Buddhist Sculpture*, Tokyo, 1995, plates volume 1, plate 220 for a marble three-storey pagoda, dated to 532; and plate 95a for a sandstone fragmentary example.

Wang Fengjun, 'Stone Pagodas with Carved Figures Dated to the Northern, Sui and Tang Dynasties in Xi'an Region', *Kaogu yu Wenwu*, volume 4, Xi'an, 2011, page 90, figure 2, for a Northern Wei example discovered in the Li Quan Temple site, in the southern suburbs of Xi'an.

二五 红砂岩法轮阁 北魏 正光年铭 应为公元五二〇年

高 三〇·五公分

红砂岩，长方形许愿碑，双层塔式，拱瓦飞檐，下承矮长方形基座，座周长面刻枝叶纹，短面刻盘龙纹。下层正面佛龛，浮雕浅刻，佛结跏趺坐，手施无畏印，身着僧袍，前开胸式，窄褶遍体，头光硕大，光线四射。两侧各有三座小佛龛，内刻思维佛。上层两侧，都刻以单层拱形佛龛中一对坐佛，应为释迦和多宝佛。下层侧面窄细，均为单龛，立佛合十像与弥勒交腿像各据一面。上层两侧，都刻以单

凤图案。此阁阴面三十三字铭文，字居框中。

The inscription on the reverse cannot be deciphered on the upper storey but reads as follows on the lower storey:

大魏正光元年六月九日奉皇帝陛下令造善光法轮阁之安镇

which may be translated as:

On the ninth day, the sixth month of the first year of the Zhengguang reign of the Great Northern Wei [corresponding to 520], His Majesty the Emperor commissioned a Bright and Virtuous Buddhist Wheel Pavilion to bring peace.

Chinese Buddhist votive steles of the fifth and sixth centuries are to be found in a wide variety of forms and materials (for instance limestone, marble, serpentine, as well as sandstone) and often show a range of influences ranging from Indian votive stupas to Han period commemorative tablets. The present example, combining the Chinese 'tiled' roofs of a pagoda with recessed niche images, such as those originally found in cave temples, displays a thorough integration of imported Buddhist ideas with traditional Chinese elements. Unlike the earlier Han tablets, Buddhist steles were not subject to sumptuary laws and were commissioned by a wide cross section of the community, from the upper classes to 'grassroots devotional societies of significant size, encompassing patrons of different social strata.'[1]

[1] Dorothy C. Wong, Chinese Steles, Pre-Buddhist and Buddhist Use of a Symbolic Form, Honolulu, 2004, page 64.

## 26
## Bronze Buddha
*Western Wei period, inscribed with date corresponding to 539*
*Height: 28.0cm*

Bronze hollow-cast figure of Buddha Shakyamuni seated in *virasana* on a waisted Sumeru throne supported on a four-legged pedestal, his right hand raised in *abhaya mudra* and left hand in *varada mudra*. The slender, elongated figure is dressed in monastic robes, which cover both shoulders, with undergarment tied at the front and torso partially exposed, and falling in U-shaped pleats at the front, the hems cascading in stylized, flaring folds past the top of the throne. His long, narrow face, with half-closed eyes and pointed nose, wears a contemplative expression and his finely incised hair is neatly dressed, covering the prominent *ushnisha*. The back of the figure is flat with a projection for the attachment of a mandorla. The waisted throne is supported on a pedestal with four flaring legs, the front, back and sides incised with a fifty-six-character inscription. The figure bears a lustrous brownish-green patina.

Provenance:

James Freeman, Kyoto.

Norman A. Kurland, U. S. A.

Exhibited:

Harvard, Cambridge, Massachusetts, 2001, Harvard University Art Museums.

Similar examples:

S. Matsubara, *A History of Chinese Buddhist Sculpture*, Tokyo, 1995, plates volume 1, plate 223, for a bronze Buddha seated in the European position; and plate 259b for a stone stele with a very similar figure of a seated Buddha, dated to 540.

二六

铜佛坐像　西魏　大统年铭

高　二八・〇公分

应为公元五三九年

青铜质，中空铸造，释迦摩尼像，结跏趺坐于束腰须弥台上，下承四腿基座。佛右手抬起施无畏印，左手施与愿印。佛面长且窄，眼眸半闭，尖鼻子，体型修长，身着袈裟，覆盖双肩，胸部半露，僧祇支系结于前，弯曲皱褶从前垂落，波纹衣襟，顺畅展开，流过宝座。佛面长且窄，眼眸半闭，尖鼻子，思维神态，发纹清晰，盖住高肉髻。像背平坦，有凸出处安装背光。束腰宝座下，四腿外展，前后及侧面刻有五十六字铭文。此像有光泽熠熠的褐绿锈层。

136

The inscription on the pedestal reads as follows:

大统五年, 岁在己未, 六月癸未, 朔二日, 永川寺比丘惠樂, 造释迦摩尼像一躯, 仰为皇帝陛下, 七世所生, 因缘眷属, 法界众生, 住静佛国, 咸同此愿

which may be translated as:

The fifth year of Datong, the *jiwei* year, on the second day of the sixth month, [corresponding to 539], the Monk Huile of Yongchuan Temple commissioned this image of Shakyamuni Buddha in the hope that the Emperor, ancestors from seven generations, all relatives and all living beings in this world may live serenely in the Buddhist universe.

The present sculpture of the Buddha Shakyamuni, in its frontal, elongated form and cascading drapery obscuring most of the body beneath, embodies the renowned Northern Wei 'Longmen' style named after the early sixth century carvings of Buddhas, bodhisattvas and attendant figures from the Longmen cave temples in Henan province. However, what makes this figure particularly interesting is its manifestation in bronze, rather than stone, where the concern with surface embellishment, rather than volume, is especially well rendered in the cast details, such as on the pleats of the robes. Small bronze votive figures for private worship were popular at this period: the commissioning of them was considered to accrue religious merit and the figures themselves were 'assigned great potency and thus were not to be treated lightly.'[1] One of the major centres of production was Dingzhou, in Hebei province, with other centres in Shaanxi and Shanxi.

[1] Albert E. Dien, *Six Dynasties Civilization*, New Haven and London, 2007, page 409.

二七　石灰岩菩薩立像　東魏　公元五三四年─五四九年

高　六八・〇公分

石灰岩，圓雕菩薩立姿，手足殘缺，頭部微斂，腹部微隆，身體輪廓彎曲。此像雕工精細，菩薩祝福式神情，細目豐唇，微笑露渦。頭發上梳，重疊於前額，五尖頂冠，刻飾花枝紋，流蘇彎卷下墜，順肩而過。綬帶粗厚，沿著冠側，流落長耳背後。菩薩帔帛，繞肩橫腰，經兩臂下垂至膝，同時，兜提褶皺順暢，長巾繫結定在腰部。另一帶結從腰經過兜提垂下。菩薩珠寶絢爛，胸飾中含橢圓連珠飾，獅面獸周圍

27
## Limestone Bodhisattva
Eastern Wei period, 534 - 549
Height: 68.0 cm

Grey limestone standing figure of a bodhisattva carved in the round (the hands and feet now missing), shown with head gently inclined and slightly swelling stomach, thus forming a sinuous S-curve when viewed in profile, the carving throughout of exquisite delicacy. The bodhisattva has a beatific expression, with elongated eyes and full lips, dimpled at the corners and gently smiling. The hair is arranged off the forehead in overlapping layers and is crowned by a five-pointed diadem engraved with floral scrolls and falls in curling tresses over the shoulders. Thick ribbons descend from the sides of the diadem, behind the elongated ears. The deity wears a shaped shawl, wrapped around the shoulders, crossing at the waist, falling to the knees and looped over the arms, as well as a finely-pleated *dhoti* held by a knotted sash at the waist. A further knotted sash is suspended from the waist over the *dhoti*. The bodhisattva is decked with jewellery: a pectoral containing ovals set with pearls and a Buddhist lion mask surrounded by foliate motifs; a long chain, composed of beaded jewels and coral, crosses through a beaded disc at the waist and terminates at the knees. Bracelets encircle the right wrist. Pendants incorporating *bi* discs hang from the waist to each side. The sculpture, once decorated all over, in polychrome and gilding, still bears considerable traces of the original red pigment.

### Provenance:

Jui Chin Wang collection, Taibei, before 1992.

Bih Rong Wang collection, Taibei.

Eskenazi Limited, London.

Norman A. Kurland, U. S. A.

### Exhibited:

Taibei, 26 July - 19 October 1997, National Museum of History.

Kaohsiung, 2 April - 27 August 2000, Kaohsiung Museum of Fine Arts.

### Published:

National Museum of History, *The Splendour of Buddhist Statuaries – Buddhist Stone Carvings in the Northern Dynasties*, Taibei, 1997, pages 110 - 113, number 20.

Kaohsiung Museum of Fine Arts, *Ancient Chinese Sculpture II*, Kaohsiung, 2000, pages 52 - 53, number 16.

### Similar examples:

Wang Huaqing ed., *Buddhist Imagery Art at Longqing Temple of Qingzhou*, Ji'nan, 1999, plate 148 and plates 152 - 156 for a free-standing example; and plates 23 and 28 for bodhisattvas each originally part of a larger stele.

环以叶片纹，长链由联珠纹件和珊瑚条组成。在腰间交叉过连珠纹圆碟，向下止于膝盖。右腕佩戴手镯。垂饰中含玉璧自腰悬挂于另一边。此像曾彩绘并镀金，如今依旧保存部分原红色。

The bodhisattva in this exhibition is an outstanding example of Eastern Wei sculptural style, which has moved away from the linearity of Northern Wei to a more corporeal and robust presence and which continues into the Northern Qi. The additional and renewed influx of culture and ideas from India, Central and West Asia is reflected in the sculpture of this period, seen also in some of the similar examples cited above, discovered in a Buddhist hoard at Qingzhou, Shandong province.

The bodhisattva is usually described as a deity who has postponed enlightenment in order to save all beings from suffering and sorrow. The present example is remarkable for its richness of jewellery and ornamentation, partially in keeping with the stipulated iconography of the bodhisattva - the dress of an Indian prince, adorned with thirteen ornaments, including a crown, earrings, necklace, bracelets, anklets and scarves. The figure wears an elaborate pectoral around the neck, as well as a long, looped necklace, pendant discs from the waist and bracelets. The bodhisattvas discovered at Qingzhou are similarly ornamented while even more elaborate, high relief jewellery is found on the very large Northern Qi bodhisattva at the Metropolitan Museum of Art, New York.[1] The many cultural influences evident in the Northern Qi bodhisattva's jewellery, particularly the long, looped necklace, are also applicable to the present figure: 'This distinctive type of adornment exemplifies the stylistic complexities of the art of the period. While some elements can be traced to Chinese culture, others derived from northwestern India or related traditions in West Asia and Central Asia.'[2] Like the sculpture in the Metropolitan Museum, the present example wears circular discs (bi), probably intended to represent jade, suspended by sashes from the waist, traceable to the Chinese tradition. However, other influences may be perceived on the pectoral studded with cabochons encircled by pearls, from which an animal mask is suspended, similar to the necklaces on the museum example:

> 'The demon mask, in particular, reflects the influence of Khotan, a major center on the southern branch of the Silk Road. Pearls, pearl clusters, and pearl roundels, as well as stone cabochons, derive from cultures such as those of the Sassanian Empire (224 - 651), in ancient Persia, and the mercantile nation of Sogdia, in present-day Uzbekistan.'[3]

For a further discussion of the jewellery worn by the present bodhisattva, refer to the essay 'Northern Dynasties (386 - 581): Sculpture in Turbulent Times' by Annette L. Juliano, pages 24 - 25 in the present catalogue.

[1] Denise Patry Leidy and Donna Strahan, *Wisdom Embodied, Chinese Buddhist and Daoist Sculpture in the Metropolitan Museum of Art*, New York, 2010, number 9.

[2 & 3] Denise Patry Leidy and Donna Strahan, op. cit., page 76.

## 28
## Limestone Buddha
Eastern Wei or Northern Qi period, mid 6th century
Height: 49.5cm

Limestone figure of Buddha, probably originally carved into the wall of a cave and backed by a halo, the remaining fragments of which are attached to the back of the head. The deity is seated in *virasana* on a dais or throne, his right hand resting in his lap in a variant of *varada mudra*, the left hand now missing but probably once raised in *abhaya mudra*. The Buddha has a rounded face with downcast eyes, slightly smiling lips and the long ears denoting his princely heritage. His hair is arranged in tight curls and covers the cranial bump or *ushnisha*. He wears monastic robes, open at the chest, that fall in heavy folds over his arms and crossed legs – leaving the left foot bare – to hang in cascading pleats over the front of the dais. The surface of the stone bears considerable traces of red and white pigments.

Provenance:

Private collection, Mechelen, Belgium.

Eskenazi Limited, London.

Norman A. Kurland, U. S. A.

Exhibited:

London, 2014, Eskenazi Limited.

Published:

Eskenazi Limited, *Chinese sculpture c. 500 – 1500*, London, 2014, number 8.

Similar examples:

Wang Huaqing ed., *Buddhist Imagery Art at Longqing Temple of Qingzhou*, Ji'nan, 1999, numbers 91 and 92 for two larger figures of Buddha seated in *virasana* on lotus bases.

二八　石灰岩坐佛像　东魏或北齐　公元六世纪中期

高四九·五公分

石灰岩佛像，原本是雕刻在石窟壁上，从脑后遗留残迹推测，应有头光衬映。佛陀交腿而坐，或于台座上，右手置膝部，施与愿印，弯曲下垂，顺肩过腿，衣皱流畅，覆盖座前，但左脚外露。石料表面保留大量红白色块。

左手残缺，应为无畏印。佛面圆满，双目低垂，唇露微笑，长耳通灵。螺纹发鬓，遍布肉髻。身穿开胸僧衣，摺纹厚重，

Although carved almost fully in the round, the reverse of this sculpture is uneven and roughly chiselled, indicating that it was once attached to the wall of a cave, perhaps in a niche. The head may also originally have been backed by a halo. A comparison with catalogue number 16 in the present exhibition is instructive in illustrating the change in style from Northern Wei to Northern Qi. Both sculptures are of limestone, of similar size, and show Buddha seated cross-legged on a ledge looking out at the viewer, a cascade of drapery evident in front. In the present example, however, the figure wears a clinging robe, lightly carved with flowing lines, that reveals the rounded form of the body beneath, in particular the limbs. The hair is arranged in tight curls, the face is full and the right hand is carved in a gesture more naturalistic than hieratic, all features akin to the Gupta style of India that reached China both from Central Asia and by sea.[1]

[1] See Angela Falco Howard et al., *Chinese Sculpture*, New Haven and London, 2006, page 274.

29
**Limestone Torso of Buddha**
Northern Qi period, 550 - 577
Height: 35.0cm

Limestone torso and lower body of Buddha standing, with right leg slightly flexed at the knee, in *tribhanga*. The figure wears clinging robes that reveal the contours of the body, draped over the left shoulder and leaving the chest and right shoulder bare. The robe falls in shallow U-shaped folds over the stomach and between the legs and in stylized loose scrolls over both legs. The back is left plain except for the diagonally placed banded edge of the robe. The upper arms and lower legs are drilled with holes through which the rest of the arms and the feet, carved separately, would have been dowelled into position. The surface of the pale grey stone bears traces of a reddish pigment.

Provenance:

Private collection, U. S. A.

Jacques Barrère, Paris.

Eskenazi Limited, London.

Norman A. Kurland, U. S. A.

Exhibited:

Paris, 2006, Jacques Barrère.

Published:

Jacques Barrère, *Sculpture d'Asie*, Paris, 2006, pages 28 - 29.

Similar examples:

The National Museum of Chinese History, *Masterpieces of Buddhist Statuary from Qingzhou City*, Beijing, 1999, page 99, for a much larger figure carved with very similar drapery; a so, Lukas Nickel ed., *Return of the Buddha: The Qingzhou Discoveries*, London, 2002, number 24; also, Wang Huaqing ed., *Buddhist Imagery Art at Longqing Temple of Qingzhou*, Ji'nan, 1999, plate 59.

Wang Huaqing ed., *Buddhist Imagery Art at Longqing Temple of Qingzhou*, Ji'nan, 1999, plate 80.

The National Museum of Chinese History, *Masterpieces of Buddhist Statuary from Qingzhou City*, Beijing, 1999, page 101.

Yi Tongjuan ed., *Linqu fojiao zaoxiang yishu*, (The Art of Lingqu Buddhist Sculpture), Beijing, 2010, page 77, number 40 for a larger example.

Palace Museum et al., *Across the Silk Road: Gupta Sculptures and Their Chinese Counterparts during 400 - 700 AD*, Beijing, 2016, plates volume, page 397, number 182 for a larger example.

二九　石灰岩佛身　北齐　公元五五〇年—五七七年

石灰岩佛身

高 三五・〇公分

石灰岩，佛身站立姿态，右腿膝部微弯，呈三曲式。佛着贴身长袍，尽显身型。长袍自左肩斜挂，右肩及胸部裸露。长袍垂褶浅刻，弯曲形，经腹部腿间，松散纹于两腿之上。像背除了长袍后沿刻纹外，无其他饰纹。大臂和小腿均有钻孔，意在组合分雕的臂腿部分。像表浅灰，有红色痕迹保留。

Although incomplete and small in scale, the present sculpture epitomizes Northern Qi depictions of the Buddha, as much as the well-known larger figures from Qingzhou. In contrast to the angular forms, frontal poses and highly intricate draperies common to both the stone and bronze representations of Buddha in the Northern Wei period, as seen in catalogue number 16 of the present exhibition, for example, here the body is rounded with an indication of movement. Its form is revealed rather than hidden by the clinging drapery that is lightly incised with flowing folds. The Northern Wei emperors were particularly keen to emphasise their status as the natural heirs of all things Han Chinese, including both language and dress, to which the stiff, heavy forms seen on sculpture of the period are related. The Northern Qi, on the other hand, admired aspects of non-Chinese culture and the drapery forms seen on the present sculpture, and many others of the period, undoubtedly derive from Northern India.[1]

[1] See Su Bai, 'Sculpture of the Northern Qi Dynasty and Its Stylistic Models', in Lukas Nickel ed., *Return of the Buddha: The Qingzhou Discoveries*, London, 2002, pages 54 - 59, for a more detailed exposition.

绿乳釉色，白胎盖罐，器呈球形，宽沿内卷，外饰三道弦纹，圈足结实外展。主体有七片联珠纹边的椭圆贴饰，各含中亚舞者或乐手演奏琵琶及笛子的形象，以凸鼓点组成的竖纹间隔。中部上下均以凸点纹的横线围住，向外又一圈鼓起点点环绕，第三道点纹线则位于腹部。器盖圆拱形，花蕾式盖钮，盖面饰以鼓起点，联珠纹环边。除底部烧结痕外，整器覆以透明乳黄釉，叶绿色竖条，盖面绿釉偏重，色泽闪烁，底部素胎。

三〇　绿釉陶圆盖罐　北齐　公元五五〇年—五七七年

高一二·〇公分

## 30

**Glazed Earthenware Jar and Cover**
Northern Qi period, 550 - 577
Height: 12.0cm

Green- and cream-glazed white earthenware jar and cover, the jar of spherical form, with wide incurving mouth encircled by a triple line border, supported on a solid, flared foot. The central register comprises seven oval appliqués with beaded (*lianzhu*) borders, each containing a Central Asian dancer in animated posture or a musician playing either a lute (*pipa*) or a transverse flute *(di)*, each separated by a vertical line of raised dots of slip. The register is enclosed above and below by a horizontal beaded border and another of applied, pointed dots of slip. A third beaded border encircles the lower body. The circular cover, of flattened domed shape, with a bud-shaped knop, is also decorated with applied dots within beaded borders. The entire vessel, except for the spur marks on the base, is covered with a transparent yellowish-cream glaze, vertically streaked with leaf-green while the cover is glazed a darker green glaze with some iridescence, its underside unglazed.

Provenance:

J. J. Lally & Co, New York.

Norman A. Kurland, U. S. A.

Similar example:

Lu Zhangshen ed., *Zhongguo gudai ciqi yishu*, (The Art of Ancient Chinese Ceramics), Hefei, 2011, pages 64 - 65, number 22.

The dancers and musicians contained within the beaded medallions of the present jar are, despite their small scale, clearly shown as entertainers from Central Asia, with pronounced features and distinctive clothing and head-gear. Performers from Central Asia and from Sogdiana in particular, were in demand as their music became increasingly popular in China. Central Asian dance was, by the Tang period, termed *huteng* (barbarian leap) or 'Sogdian whirl' to describe the animated movements and gyrations. The *pipa* or lute being played by two of the musicians on this jar was most probably a Central Asian import.[1]

Scenes of such entertainment were clearly a source of great fascination in the Northern Qi period and have also been found carved on sixth century sarcophagi, some perhaps belonging to Central Asians living in China at this period. One such is the marble sarcophagus, discovered in Taiyuan, Shanxi province, of Yu Hong (533/534 - 92), who was of Turkic or Sogdian origin, born in north-west China. One of the main panels is carved with the scene of a couple feasting, as they are entertained by a Central Asian dancer and a group of kneeling musicians, while the base is carved with further pairs of musicians.[2] Similar scenes of revelry are also found on the panels of a late sixth to early seventh century funerary bed, now in the Miho Museum, Japan.[3]

Another remarkable feature, apparently specific to this period, is the decorative technique on the present jar of raised dots of slip: smaller, pointed dots (forming a beaded border) and larger disc-like dots. Related to the present jar and cover are two vessels, a lead-glazed white bowl and a green-glazed stem cup, both in the collection of the Tokiwayama Bunko Foundation, with surface decoration of raised dots and discs.[4] The larger discs on the vessels were apparently formed in a two-stage process: 'First, small flat disks were applied to the body and then sharply pointed cones were added on top of the disks.'[5] Such wares, apparently imitating glass or metalwork, are rare, although an example - a brown-glazed bowl with raised cream dots – was excavated from a Northern Wei site at Luoyang, Henan province.[6]

[1] Albert E. Dien, *Six Dynasties Civilization*, New Haven and London, 2007, page 342 - 343.

[2] Cao Yin, Edmund Capon et al., *A Silk Road Saga, The Sarcophagus of Yu Hong*, Sydney, 2013, pages 48 - 50; and pages 60 - 61.

[3] Miho Museum ed., *Miho Museum, South Wing*, Shiga, 1997, number 125.

[4] Gakuji Hasebe et al., *The Bulletin of the Chinese Ceramic Study Association of Tokiwayama Bunko Foundation*, volume 3, Northern Qi Ceramics, Tokyo, 2010, number 5, for the Northern Qi white bowl and number 6 for the Northern Qi/Sui stem cup.

[5] Gakuji Hasebe et al., op. cit., page 133 and page 23 for comparable examples.

[6] James Watt et al., *China, Dawn of a Golden Age, 200 – 750 AD*, New York, 2004, number 160.

三一

青釉陶人面纹罐　北齐　公元五五〇年—五七七年

高　二六・〇公分

绿釉褐胎　束腰长颈　口沿外翻　器身扁球状　高圈足外展。器体遍施各类贴花饰，中间一圈尤为醒目。其中四张人面纹，应属中亚男性，长发中分，眉毛浓重，高颧大耳，张口露齿，髭浓髯短。四具狮面饰于人面之间，獠牙尖利，口中衔环。人兽间以联珠圈流苏饰纹隔开。此种流苏纹四件，重复使用于圈足的外部，与四组花蕾枝蔓相映成趣。同时，四件倒贴于口沿外壁，呈别具一格的上喷图案。长颈

## 31
### Green-glazed Earthenware Jar
Northern Qi period, 550 - 577
Height: 26.0cm

Green-glazed reddish-buff earthenware jar with waisted trumpet neck, everted, grooved rim and compressed, globular body supported on a high, flared, foot. The vessel is richly ornamented with moulded appliqués, the most striking of which encircle its central section. They consist of four Central Asian male faces resembling masks, with parted hair, bushy eyebrows, bulging cheeks, large ears, mouths open to show their teeth, luxuriant moustaches and tiny goatee beards. The faces alternate with four appliqués modelled as lion masks, each with two sharp front teeth, holding ring handles in their mouths. The human and animal masks are interspersed with applied motifs resembling tasselled pearls issuing from beaded roundels, or perhaps representing flowing water. Four of these tasselled motifs are repeated around the foot - alternating with four motifs incorporating bud forms and scrolls – and four are repeated below the rim, the composition turned on its head. The lower part of the neck, below three raised rings, is decorated with four palmette appliqués with bud, leaf and scroll motifs. Below these, the shoulder of the vessel is set with a row of mounted hemispherical studs, imitating pearls or jewels, within raised lines. The entire exterior of the vase and interior of the neck are covered with a green lead glaze, stippled with patches of ochre and brown, and iridescent in areas. The high foot has a circular opening in its underside.

Provenance:

Eskenazi Limited, London.

Norman A. Kurland, U. S. A.

Exhibited:

London, 2008, Eskenazi Limited.

Published:

Eskenazi Limited, *Chinese ceramics and stone sculpture*, London, 2008, number 2.

Giuseppe Eskenazi in collaboration with Hajni Elias, *A Dealer's Hand, The Chinese Art Market Through the Eyes of Giuseppe Eskenazi*, London, 2012, page 162, figure 153.

Similar examples:

John Ayers, *The Tsui Museum of Art*, Hong Kong, 1991, number 8, for a larger example of slightly different shape, now in the Metropolitan Museum of Art, New York; also, Clarence Shangraw, *The Tsui Museum of Art, Chinese Ceramics 1, Neolithic to Liao*, Hong Kong, 1993, number 63; also, Christie's, London, *Fine Chinese Ceramics, Bronzes, Jades and Works of Art*, 4 December 1995, number 55; also, Zhang Deqin et al., *Splendour of Ancient Chinese Art, Selections from the Collections of T. T. Tsui Galleries of Chinese Art Worldwide*, Hong Kong, 1996, number 12; also, further discussed in detail and illustrated by Suzanne G. Valenstein, 'Preliminary Findings on a 6th-Century Earthenware Jar', *Oriental Art*, volume XLlll,

下部饰以三道凸纹，下饰四组花蕾叶片贴花饰。之下器肩环施乳钉纹宽带一周。外壁及颈内遍施绿铅釉，部分有浅黄色斑和棕色及彩虹色。

高圈足平坦，底部有圆形开孔。

number 4 (1997/8), Singapore, 1997, pages 2 - 13; also, Suzanne G. Valenstein, *Cultural Convergence in the Northern Qi Period: A Flamboyant Chinese Ceramic Container*, New York, 2007, page 100, plate 16 and page 126, plate 74.

Sotheby's, London, *Fine Chinese and Korean Ceramics and Works of Art*, 9 June 1992, number 92, for the jar now in the Royal Ontario Museum, Toronto; also, Royal Ontario Museum, *The T. T. Tsui Galleries of Chinese Art*, Toronto, 1996, number 60, where the height is wrongly given as 44.9cm rather than 35.3cm; also, Giuseppe Eskenazi in collaboration with Hajni Elias, *A Dealer's Hand, The Chinese Art Market Through the Eyes of Giuseppe Eskenazi*, London, 2012, page 252, plate 199.

The present jar is extremely rare and is one of three published examples of this type, two of which are in museum collections – the Metropolitan Museum of Art and the Royal Ontario Museum - as cited above. While vessels of this form clearly had their roots in the Han lead-glazed earthenware tradition, the influx of motifs, ideas and stylistic vocabulary during the fifth and sixth centuries into China is also on exuberant display on the present jar.

Similarities with Han *hu* vessels – which ultimately derived from bronze prototypes of the period - may be perceived, firstly, in the green glaze, recalling that of the Han dynasty; secondly, in the form of the present vessel, with its flaring neck and foot; and thirdly in the applied animal masks which recall those on the earlier vessels, both ceramic and bronze. As has been observed by Suzanne G. Valenstein, there is also a small group of high-fired, celadon-glazed stoneware jars, with flamboyant relief-moulded appliqué decoration produced in the north in the second half of the sixth century which have stylistic similarities to the present jar.[1] These include a celadon-glazed jar with applied masks, palmettes and masks, one of four discovered from the sixth century tomb of Feng Zihui, found in Jing county, Henan province.[2] Suggested kiln sites for the production of these elaborate celadon-glazed jars include the Zhaili kiln complexes near Zibo, Shandong province, as well as the Xing kiln complexes in Neiqiu county, Hebei province.[3]

Of particular fascination on the present jar, as on the Metropolitan and the Royal Ontario Museum examples, is the bold mix of appliqué designs. While the animal masks on the jar may have had an earlier ancestry in China (though they are also found in Buddhist art), some of the other motifs clearly owe their inspiration to more recent imports from Central Asia and to Buddhist iconography, as discussed by Suzanne G. Valenstein: 'Many new vessel types, as well as distinctive shapes and ornamental motifs, were taken from these foreign wares and incorporated by the Chinese into their own arts.'[4] The palmette is one motif generally regarded as being imported to China from westerly regions, frequently encountered on Buddhist sculpture and in cave temples of the fifth and sixth centuries. The beaded roundel with tasselled pearls (or flowing water) also has a Buddhist origin and may be found, for instance, on the headdress of bodhisattvas of the Northern Qi period, such as those discovered in the hoards at Qingzhou.[5] The four striking human masks – male faces with moustaches and goatee beards - encircled by pearl beading on the museum examples - are very close to motifs found on Central Asian earthenware vessels and appliqué ornaments found at Yotkan, near Khotan, on the southern rim of the Taklamakan Desert.

[1] Suzanne G. Valenstein, 'Preliminary Findings on a 6th-Century Earthenware Jar', *Oriental Art*, volume XLIII, number 4 (1997/8), Singapore, 1997, pages 2 - 13.

[2] Zhu Boqian ed., *The Complete Works of Chinese Ceramics*, volume 4, Shanghai, 2000, page 223, number 244.

[3] Suzanne G. Valenstein, op. cit. page 5.

[4] Suzanne G. Valenstein, *Cultural Convergence in the Northern Qi Period: A Flamboyant Chinese Ceramic Container*, New York, 2007, page 70.

[5] Lukas Nickel ed., *Return of the Buddha: The Qingzhou Discoveries*, London, 2002, number 31.

32
**Green-glazed Earthenware Figural Candlestick or Lamp**
Northern Qi period, 550 - 577
Height: 18.7cm

Dark-green-glazed red earthenware candlestick or lamp, the central support in the form of a kneeling figure. The upper section comprises a tubular socket presumably for holding a candle, on a circular, shallow drip tray with low, flaring edges, supported on the head of a powerful kneeling Atlantid, modelled fully in the round. His rounded face has large almond-shaped eyes, broad nose, wide mouth and furrowed forehead, framed by a neatly fitting headdress, from the sides of which his pendulous ears emerge. His bunched, muscular arms, either side of a pronounced pot-belly, terminate in large hands resting on his knees. His back is well modelled with powerful bare shoulders, with a cloth covering his buttocks. The figure kneels, legs folded beneath his thighs, within an incised circle on the lower, larger drip tray which is raised on a hollow, flaring foot. The candlestick is entirely covered, apart from the underside of the foot, with a rich green glaze, varying in tone from olive to leaf green. Neat rows of cream-coloured dots of slip encircle the outer rim and the interior base of the drip trays, as well as the rim of the socket, which is further decorated with a second band of smaller dots.

Provenance:

J. J. Lally and Co., New York.

Norman A. Kurland, U. S. A.

Similar examples:

Sotheby's, London, *Important Early Chinese Ceramics, Archaic Bronzes, Sculpture, Silver and Lacquer from the Works of Art Collection of the British Rail Pension Fund*, 12 December 1989, number 50, for a glazed stoneware figural lamp.

Matsuoka Museum of Art, *Toyo toji meihin toroku*, (Selected Masterpieces of Oriental Ceramics), Tokyo, 1991, page 11, number 5, for a candlestick from the Yueyao kilns, the kneeling support figure of a 'foreigner' glazed in dark brown.

Regina Krahl, *Chinese Ceramics from the Meiyintang Collection*, volume 3 (I), London, 2006, number 1235, for a very similar tray, supporting a jar and cover, decorated in the same manner.

三二

绿釉陶人形烛台

北齐　公元五五〇年—五七七年

高 一八·七公分

深绿釉，红胎烛台，中间为跪奴支撑。上部包括管状烛座，圆平浅烛台，边沿外翻，下承于跪奴头部。此俑体格健壮，圆脸大眼，宽鼻阔嘴，前额皱起，头饰整齐，大耳下垂，双臂肌肉鲜明，大腹便便，手掌巨大，附于膝盖。他的背部有力，双肩赤裸，衣盖臀部。此俑屈腿，跪于大型托盘之上，盘下圈足，内空且外展。除足底素胎外，此器通体覆以绿釉，密实厚重，色调多变。烛台托盘的外沿和盘内，

均以乳色点纹圈装饰，烛座口沿外饰纹亦同，下附加小点饰纹一周。

The present lamp, the support in the form of a kneeling Atlantid figure – perhaps a dwarf or a mythical being, with exaggerated non-Han features - is a reflection of the influx of fresh ideas and motifs entering China from Central Asia during the sixth century combining with an existing tradition. From the Warring States period onwards, lamps were of significance in a mortuary context, not just as a source of illumination, but also as an important tool for the deceased in their journey in the afterlife: 'lamps often counted as travel paraphernalia, to be used to illuminate the post-mortem journey to the world beyond'[1] and it is most likely that in the sixth century the inclusion of such earthenware lamps in tombs performed a similar function.

For a discussion of the unusual use of raised dots of slip as decoration on sixth century earthenware pieces refer to the footnote of catalogue number 30.

[1] Catalogue entry by Guolong Lai in Cary Liu et al., *Recarving China's Past, Art, Archaeology, and Architecture of the "Wu Family Shrines"*, Princeton, 2005, pages 223 - 225.

## 33

## Two Painted Earthenware Hounds

Six Dynasties period, mid 6th century
Length: 25.3cm and 20.1cm

Two hollow buff earthenware hounds, each on an irregularly shaped base. The larger hound, with a thickset, powerful body, rangy limbs and curling tail, lies on its front, leaning to its right, intently gnawing with sharp teeth on a hunk of meat wedged between its massive paws. Its finely modelled head, with large floppy ears and rounded, expressive eyes in deep sockets, is distinguished by a central white stripe down the forehead and muzzle, further accentuated by an incised line. White markings – around the neck, on the belly and on the haunches – stand out against its dark coat. Its smaller companion, possibly female, lies in a characteristic alert canine pose with crossed paws, its chest picked out in reddish-pink against its white coat. It wears a placid expression with the flattened ears, open mouth and lolling tongue. An incised line runs from its forehead to its muzzle and further incised lines indicate its brow and the folds of the mouth. Extensive remains of black, white, red and pink pigments are visible on both figures.

Provenance:

Priestley and Ferraro, London.

Eskenazi Limited, London.

Norman A. Kurland, U. S. A.

Exhibited:

London, 1999, Priestley and Ferraro.

Harvard, Cambridge, Massachusetts, 2000-1, Harvard University Art Museums.

Published:

Priestley and Ferraro, *Out of Wind and Dust*, London, 1999, number 9.

Similar examples:

Harriet McNamee, *Chinese Art from the Ferris Luboshez Collection*, University of Maryland, 1972, number 65, figure 28.

Tenri University Sankokan Museum, *Tenri hizo meihin-ten*, (Exhibition of Masterworks from the Tenri Museum), Osaka, 1992, page 99, plate 329, for a pair of hounds, one eating and the other scratching itself.

Patricia Berger and Jennifer R. Casler, *Tomb Treasures from China; The Buried Art of Ancient Xi'an*, San Francisco and Fort Worth, 1994, number 35, for a recumbent dog with crossed paws, excavated from Hongguang village, Changlingxiang, Ankang county.

Regina Krahl, *Evolution to Perfection: Chinese Ceramics from the Meiyintang Collection*, London, 1996, number 39; also Regina Krahl, *Chinese Ceramics from the Meiyintang Collection*, volume 3 (I), London, 2006, number 1166.

三三

两只彩绘陶狗

六朝 公元六世纪中期

长 二五·三公分 二〇·一公分

浅黄陶胎，空心塑猎狗一对，不规则形底座。大狗体态粗壮雄健，四肢修长，长尾曲卷，趴前靠右。前掌肥大，按住肉块，利牙大啃，前爪交叠，前胸红粉色，衬以白地。其神态平和，双耳放松，嘴部微张，卷舌外伸。线纹从额头延至口吻，眉毛用线条勾勒，嘴有皱褶。两狗大部颜色保留完好，黑白红粉清晰可辨。

浅黄陶胎，空心塑猎狗一对，不规则形底座。大狗体态粗壮雄健，四肢修长，长尾曲卷，趴前靠右。前掌肥大，按住肉块，利牙大啃，颈间腹部后腿白色环绕，与余部黑色，相符相宜，交映生辉。另一狗略小，或为母狗，摆出特有的趴卧姿势，前爪交叠，前胸红粉色，衬以白地。其神态平和，双耳放松，嘴部微张，卷舌外伸。狗头精雕细作，软片大耳，圆眼深陷，炯炯有神，额头到吻部，有中心白色条，并加刻线纹以强调。神态专注。

Domesticated in China from the Shang period or earlier, dogs had multiple purposes: to guard homes, to hunt, to act as companions and perhaps, as food and for ritual sacrifice. As discussed by Virginia Bower, James Legge's translation of the *Liji* (Book of Rites) highlights two types of dog distinguished by function, while a late sixth/early seventh century commentary on the *Liji* by Kong Yingda points to an undesignated third:

> 'only two sorts of dogs are mentioned, and they are distinguished by function: the *shouquan* (literally, "protective" dog) and the *tianquan* (literally, "field" dog, i.e. a hunting dog). Kong's commentary mentions a third type of dog, *shiquan*, dogs for eating or sacrificing. *Liji* often mentions the eating or sacrificing of dogs, but does not seem to contain a designation for these canine victims. To summarize the *Liji* and Kong's commentary, dogs are of three types: the watchdog, the hunting dog, and the "food" dog. The first two were given names; the third was not.'[1]

Judging by the appearance of the present examples, they would seem to fall into the category of 'hounds' or hunting dogs, given their size and rangy limbs. However, their sympathetic and lifelike depiction would indicate that such dogs were fully integrated into the domestic context and, as tomb furnishings, would have served, not just as 'hunt' or 'guard' dogs but also as faithful companions in the afterlife.

[1] Catalogue entry on dogs, particularly in the Eastern Han period, by Virginia Bower in Cary Liu et al., *Recarving China's Past, Art, Archaeology, and Architecture of the "Wu Family Shrines"*, Princeton, 2005, pages 433 - 440.

34
# Two Painted Earthenware Caparisoned Horses
Northern Qi period, 550 - 577
Height: 63.0 and 58.0cm

Two large painted grey earthenware caparisoned hollow horses on trapezoidal bases, each depicted in mid-stride, with proper right leg leading and lavishly ornamented with elaborately modelled trappings and fittings. Each horse is depicted in an alert and lively posture, the slender, arched neck turned to its proper left, supporting a finely modelled head with pricked ears, flaring nostrils and forelock tied into a tufted top-knot and wearing a bridle composed of straps, studs and a floral plaque pressed against the muzzle.

The mane on the larger horse is painted in dark red within scalloped borders, extending down either side of the neck while a double plaited strap, knotted beneath the chin, encircles the top of the neck. The breast strap is ornamented with tear-shaped pendants with moulded flowerheads and secured with a buckle. The rump is applied with rounded studs with moulded flowerheads and is encircled by the crupper strap from which bell-shaped tassels hang; three flower-shaped plaques are suspended just above the long, well-groomed tail. A blue and red striped blanket with knotted ends is thrown over, and partially obscures, the saddle, a striped tiger skin and the protective flaps.

The smaller horse has a well-defined mane, falling in thick, wavy locks on either side of the slender neck, and a large pointed tassel hangs beneath its chin. The breast strap is hung with rounded ornaments decorated with moulded flowerheads and secured with a buckle. The rump is decorated with a central flowerhead from which radiate plaited straps, alternating with floral trappings; the crupper strap, with bell-shaped tassels runs under the long well-groomed tail. A striped blanket with knotted ends is thrown over the saddle, the saddle pad and the flaps. Extensive remains of white, red, blue, black, green and brown pigments are visible on both the horses and many of the trappings are gilded.

Provenance:

Eskenazi Limited, London.

Norman A. Kurland, U. S. A.

Similar examples:

'Hebei Cixian Beiqi Gao Run mu', (The Northern Qi Tomb of Gao Run, Ci county, Hebei province), *Kaogu*, volume 3, Beijing, 1979, plate 8, figure 2 and page 240 for a line drawing of a smaller example.

Cultural Centre of Cixian, 'Excavation of the Eastern Wei Tomb of the Princess of the Ruru Nationality at Cixian in Hebei', *Wenwu*, volume 4, Beijing, 1984, plate 5, figure 2 and page 6 for a line drawing.

Lin Shuzhong ed., *Zhongguo meishu quanji, diaosu bian 3, Wei Jin nanbeichao diaosu*, (The Great Treasury of Chinese Art, Sculpture 3, Six Dynasties), Beijing, 1988, page 156, number 132 for the upper part of a large caparisoned horse from the tomb of Fan Cui (died 575), Luoyang, Henan province.

Robert D. Jacobsen, *Celestial Horses and Long Sleeve Dancers, The David W. Dewey Collection of Ancient Chinese Tomb Sculpture*, Minneapolis, 2013, pages 142 - 143.

For an example in the Minneapolis Institute of Art see:
https://collections.artsmia.org/art/95826/striding-horse-china

三四 两匹彩绘陶马 北齐 公元五五○年—五七七年

高 六三·○公分 五八·○公分

灰陶胎，空心塑造，此对马体型高大，呈踱步形，右腿前行，底座梯形，马具装点豪华精美。马匹姿态优雅而警觉，细颈弯拱，扭头向左，头部竖耳，鼻翼张开，额鬃紧束，向上高耸，鬐头上有革带及饰钉，一块花饰牌，粘贴于吻部。大马的背鬃施以深红色，波纹形边，并扩展至颈部。颈部双编带扎在颔下，绕颈一周。攀胸上挂一组心形饰物，其表有花蕾纹，并以带扣加固。后臀上圆泡饰，表面花蕾纹，环

This pair of magnificent horses have a number of features in common with the smaller caparisoned horses typical of the Northern Wei period.[1] These include the strong curving necks of the horses, the red painted mane with scalloped border (on one of the horses), the knotted saddle blanket over the saddle and the elaborate trappings. However, the large size of these horses and the liveliness of their postures, conveying a sense of movement, distinguish them from their more stylized and essentially static Northern Wei counterparts.

A particular feature of both these horses are the elaborate trappings, perhaps Western Asian in origin, lavish in quantity and richly detailed in finish. The extensive remains of gilding on the breast and crupper ornaments, studs, pendants and the buckles indicate the original versions would have been made of gilt bronze, while the fine details on the straps indicate they might have been plaited or finely striated leather. The extensive moulded decorative elements on the horses' rumps – on one covering the entire surface and on the other, comprising elements secured by radiating straps – seem to be a feature mostly confined to the sixth and seventh centuries. By the Tang period, such lavish and varied ornamentation seems to have given way to a more standard repertoire: for instance, a single rump ornament (*jisheng*) held in place by radiating straps or the 'apricot leaf' ornaments placed on the crupper and breast straps.

The present figures testify to the importance in which horses were held during the Six Dynasties period. In addition to their significance to the military during this time of continuous warfare, horses were clearly symbols of power and affluence and it is likely that these grand models were intended for the tomb of a high-ranking individual, probably a member of the ruling elite, who had perhaps owned such horses in his or her lifetime.

[1] See catalogue number 23.

以辔带，带上挂钟形流苏，三块花板吊于长尾之上。绘以蓝红条的毛毯，覆盖马上，两端系结。马鞍虎纹，障泥护体。小马鬃毛梳理完好，间以花叶带

搭垂细颈两侧，发缕粗波状，大流苏挂颈下。攀胸悬一组心形饰物，表面花蕾纹，有带扣固定。臀部中花蕾纹为心，编带四散，间以花叶带

。辔带经马尾下，带上悬钟形流苏。彩带毛毯覆盖鞍子，系结于端。鞍垫绿色和红色，障泥外挺。两马大部白色，红色，蓝色，黑色，绿色

及褐色清晰可见，许多饰带上金彩明显。

170

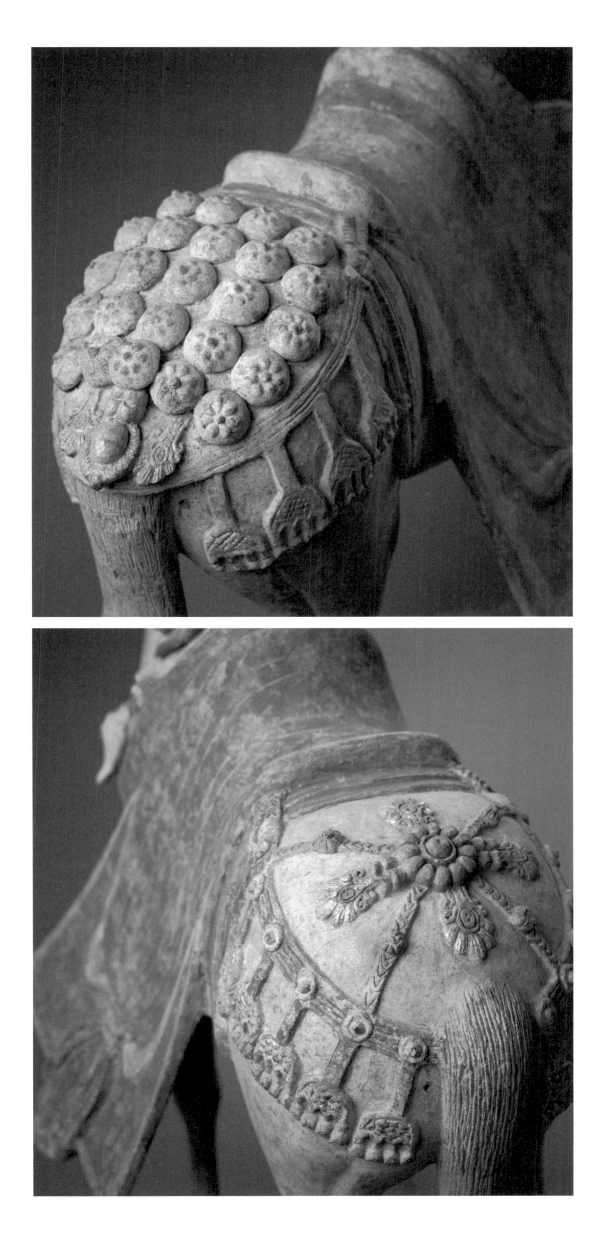

35
Painted and Gilt Marble Stele
Northern Qi period, 550 - 577
Height: 65.0cm

Painted and gilt white marble stele, carved in openwork with figures under and among the branches of a double gingko tree, the overlapping leaves of which form the arched outer edge of the sculpture, all supported on a carved rectangular base. The central image is of a deity in pensive attitude (*siwei*), right leg raised, left leg pendant, right elbow resting on the right knee, fingers of the right hand once touching the cheek. The deity wears a crown, necklaces, bracelets and a *dhoti*, the head backed by a circular halo. Above are six *apsaras* in tiered flight, carrying a looping beaded garland, bearing aloft the seated figure of Amitabha Buddha. To each side of the central figure stand a pair of luohans, a pair of Pratyeka Buddhas and a pair of bodhisattvas on stemmed lotus pods, held by jaws of sinuous dragons and, below them, a single dignitary to each side. The base is carved in high relief with a guardian figure, *vajrapani*, at each end and a pair of confronted Buddhist lions. Below, two small plump, kneeling Atlantids hold up a bud-shaped *boshanlu* amid lotus flowers.

The reverse of the sculpture shows the branches and fan-shaped leaves of the gingko trees arranged as four arched rows framing the back of the deity. Against each trunk stands a figure, possibly a donor, with folded hands concealed within long sleeves. A cowled, seated figure is carved against the lower part of the lotus throne. On the base, to either side of an undecorated rectangular area perhaps intended for an inscription, is seated the Tree Spirit King to the proper right and the Mountain Spirit King to the proper left, wearing knee-length boots, each raising a flaming jewel.

The short sides of the base are carved with scenes of great interest. On the proper right, a figure (perhaps Buddha), with right hand raised in a gesture of blessing, mounted on a lion, approaches the back of a monkey-like figure that stands over a kneeling human in an attitude of benediction. The proper left side is carved with four figures of secular appearance. The two larger, probably from their clothes one male, the other female, each raise a thick-stemmed lotus in the right hand whilst holding on to a smaller figure, possibly a child, with the left. Perhaps this scene represents, as a family, the donors or commissioners of the sculpture.

The sculpture is remarkable for the extent of painted decoration that still remains, adding another dimension entirely to the carving, in some areas continuing in painting where the carving stops. Decorated with particular delicacy are the lotus throne, the halo and the most unusual key-fret border (*huiwen*) around the base. The underside of the base has been partly hollowed out.

Provenance:

Chan Kam Po of Hang Cheong Company, Macau (purchased 1976).

Private collection, Japan.

Eskenazi Limited, London.

Norman A. Kurland, U. S. A.

Published:

Giuseppe Eskenazi in collaboration with Hajni Elias, *A Dealer's Hand, The Chinese Art Market Through the Eyes of Giuseppe Eskenazi*, London, 2012, page 165, figure 157.

三五

描金透雕理石思維像

高 六五 · ○公分

北齐 公元五五○年 — 五七七年

白理石，透雕佛像碑，佛众散于双株银杏树下，叶片重叠，形成拱形，成为佛像的外边缘，下承长方形基座。中心像是弥勒佛像，坐在莲花座上，深沉思维状，右腿抬起，左腿下垂，善跏趺坐。右肘支撑于右膝，右手指曾贴在腮部。弥勒头戴宝冠，颈佩项圈，双手带镯，身穿兜提，头依光环。六个飞天分层起舞，手捧花篮，珠光宝气，高处坐阿弥陀佛。弥勒的两侧莲花蕾中，有弯曲的龙身，还有两尊罗汉，两

尊圆觉佛，两尊菩萨，之下两边各有一官员。基座高浮雕制，二位护法金刚，各占一端，一手持宝杵。两只佛狮相对。弥勒佛脚下，两个跪奴侍候博山炉，炉旁莲花围绕。背阴显示银杏树干，叶茂如扇，弥勒佛后有四拱形位。树干边各靠一人，或许是施主，长袖笼手。一冠冕者坐于佛座下部。座中有长方形，区内素纹，或许准备刻铭处，树精王交叉腿坐于右边，山精王在左边，下穿及膝长靴，都有火焰珠。基座短面雕刻情景有趣，右侧一位或为佛陀，坐于狮子之上，右手施以祝愿印，接近一神猿的身后，猿亦有祝福神态，下有一跪地人。左侧刻画四位俗人形象，两位大些的，从衣着看，应是一男一女，每人右手持粗茎莲花，左手抱一小孩。也许是捐赠者或造像人的家庭写照。

Similar examples:

René-Yvon Lefebvre d'Argencé ed., *Chinese, Korean and Japanese Sculpture in the Avery Brundage Collection*, San Francisco, 1974, number 56, for a similar stele inscribed with a date corresponding to 551.

S. Matsubara, *A History of Chinese Buddhist Sculpture*, Tokyo, 1995, volume 2, plate 424, for an example in the Hebei Provincial Museum; also, Tokyo National Museum, *Treasures of Ancient China*, Tokyo, 2000, number 141.

S. Matsubara, *A History of Chinese Buddhist Sculpture*, Tokyo, 1995, volume 2, plate 393a, for a smaller example in the Tokyo National Museum; also, Osaka Municipal Museum, *Chinese Buddhist Stone Sculpture, Veneration of the Sublime*, Osaka, 1995, page 102, plate 113.

Palace Museum ed., *Compendium of Collections in the Palace Museum, Sculpture*, volume 7, (Buddhist Figures Unearthed at the Site of Xiude Temple in Quyang, Hebei Province), Beijing, 2011, plate 156, for a very similar, but fragmented example inscribed with a date corresponding to 557; and for others, plates 157 and 159.

The present sculpture is remarkable for its sensuous carving, wealth of iconographic detail and the luminous quality of the marble combined with the distinctive openwork detail. It is likely that the marble of the present sculpture was quarried in Quyang, part of the Taihang mountain range along the border of present-day south-west Hebei or south-east Shanxi and then worked in Dingxian or Quyang, a centre for the production of Buddhist marble sculpture between the sixth and the eighth centuries. The sculpture workshops of this area were innovative, as has been described by Angela Falco Howard:

> 'Artisans from Zhengding and Dingzhou Counties (near present-day Shijiazhuang, Hebei) working with local micaceous marble used perforation to create uncommonly intricate steles. The process was particularly effective in executing aureoles, which as backdrops to the seated or standing images, were transformed into leafy screens with the lightness of lace.'[1]

Howard continues to discuss a related openwork marble stele excavated in Gaocheng, Hebei, now in the Longxing Temple, Zhengding county, commissioned by a nun of the Jianzhong Temple in 562; the similarities between the two would suggest that stylistically, the present sculpture could be dated to the second half of the sixth century. The marble itself and the features of the carving also relate it to a group of marble Buddhist steles and sculptures, some dated late sixth century, unearthed at the site of the Xiude temple in Quyang, Hebei province, as cited in the similar examples above.

The iconography of the 'pensive' figure, seated with right hand raised to right cheek and one leg resting on the knee of the pendant leg, became very popular during the fifth and sixth centuries in China. The posture, often described as *siwei*, came to mean deep contemplation or serious thought and during the Northern and Southern Dynasties sculptures were at times designated by inscription as *siwei* figures. Such figures have been much discussed by modern scholars, amongst them Denise Patry Leidy and Eileen Hsu. A consensus has yet to be reached as to the identity of the figure, sometimes identified as the young Prince Siddhartha before his enlightenment or Maitreya, the bodhisattva of the future, preaching in the Tusita heaven. However, it has been suggested by Leidy for instance that the pensive bodhisattvas were generic visual symbols of the paradises of Maitreya and by Hsu that some of the *siwei* figures represented 'actual devotees of the Maitreya cult' as an aid to meditative practice.[2]

While the identification of the main figure remains elusive, some of the other iconographic elements on this stele may be more readily identified, such as the spirit kings on the base of the reverse. This group of deities which appear in pairs or larger numbers of up to ten has been examined in detail by Emmy C. Bunker.[3] During the sixth century, they are found carved on the backs of steles and on the walls at Longmen, Gongxian and other cave temples and it has been suggested by Bunker that they had their origins in India but, once in China, may have been connected with a particular Buddhist sect that flourished during that time. The figures on the present stele, each holding a flaming pearl as attribute, are identifiable as the Tree Spirit King and the Mountain Spirit King by the tree and by the mountain behind them. Others include the Wind, Dragon, Lion, Fish, Bird, Elephant, Fire and Pearl Spirit Kings and their identification is based on inscribed names next to images on an Eastern Wei stele dated 543, now in the Isabella Stewart Gardner Museum.[4]

[1] Angela Falco Howard, *Chinese Sculpture*, New Haven and London, 2006, page 278.

[2] Eileen Hsiang-Ling Hsu, 'Visualization Meditation and the *Siwei* Icon in Chinese Buddhist Sculpture' in *Artibus Asiae*, volume LXII, Ascona, 2002, page 8.

[3] Emmy C. Bunker, 'The Spirit Kings in Sixth Century Chinese Buddhist Sculpture' in *Archives of the Chinese Art Society of America*, XVIII, New York, 1964, pages 26 - 37.

[4] For this information and much of the footnote, we are indebted to the unpublished MA thesis by Norman A. Kurland, *The Iconography of a Northern Qi Siwei Openwork Marble Stele*, London, SOAS, 2010.

三六　　石灰岩持匣佛手　　北齐　　公元五五〇年—五七七年

石灰岩，双手造型庞大，属于弟子迦叶的，手中持舍利匣。左手杯状，掌心向上，拇指弯绕，托一带圆钮的筒形器，或许为舍利匣。右手向下合掌，保护容器，手指拱起，指尖悬空。双手长指柔润，指甲圆而匀称。袖口叠褶于腕。褐色石灰岩有抛光层，保留些许红色。此像后背无雕工。

三六　响堂山石窟　河北　高　三六·六公分

## 36
## Limestone Hands

Northern Qi period, 550 - 577
Xiangtangshan cave temples, Hebei province
Height: 36.6cm

Pair of monumental limestone hands, probably belonging to a figure of Kashyapa, holding a reliquary. The left hand is cupped, with the palm held upwards and thumb curled around, supporting a cylindrical container with a rounded knop. The right hand is clasped protectively over the object, the fingers arched over, finger tips lifted. Both fleshy hands have long sensitive fingers terminating in rounded, well-shaped fingernails. The edges of the sleeves fall in folds at the wrists. The brownish stone has a softly polished patina, with traces of red pigment. The back of the sculpture is unworked.

Provenance:

Xiangtangshan cave temples, Hebei province.

K. L. Essayan collection, Paris.

Eskenazi Limited, London.

Norman A. Kurland, U. S. A.

Published:

Daijo Tokiwa and Tadashi Sekino, *Buddhist Monuments in China*, Part III, Tokyo, 1931, plate 87 for a side view of the hands of Kashyapa *in situ* at Xiangtangshan (see page 185 in the present catalogue); also, Daijo Tokiwa and Tadashi Sekino, *Shina Bunka Shiseki*, (Historical Landmarks in Chinese Culture), volume 5, Tokyo, 1939, plate 100, right.[a]

Daisy Lion-Goldschmidt and J. C. Moreau-Gobard, *Chinese Art*, Fribourg, 1960, page 276, plate 124 (published as Tang).

Wu Shuren ed., *Zhongguo diaosu yishu gaiyao*, (An Outline of Chinese Sculpture), Taibei, 1976, plate 127 (published as from Longmen).

Drouot, Paris, *Collection Essayan, Art d'Orient*, 26 April 1977, number 111 (published as from Longmen).

*Longmen liusan diaoxiang*, (Lost Statues of the Longmen Caves), Shanghai, 1993, number 88 (published as Tang).

Jin Shen, *Fojiao diaosu mingpin tulu*, (Catalogue of Famous Buddhist Sculptures), Beijing, 1997, page 421, plate 401, (published as Song).

Christie's, Paris, *Art D'Asie*, 26 November 2002, number 189 (published as Tang).

Katherine R. Tsiang, 'The Xiangtangshan Caves Project: An Overview and Progress Report with New Discoveries', *Orientations*, September 2007, Hong Kong, pages 74 - 83, figures 9 and 9a and figure 10 for the original position of the hands.

Katherine R. Tsiang et al., *Echoes of the Past, The Buddhist Cave Temples of Xiangtangshan*, Smart Museum of Art, Chicago, 2010, page 241, number 27.

Giuseppe Eskenazi in collaboration with Hajni Elias, *A Dealer's Hand, The Chinese Art Market Through the Eyes of Giuseppe Eskenazi*, London, 2012, pages 164 - 165, figure 155.

See also:

Chen Mingda, ed., *Zhongguo meishu quanji; diaosubian 13: Gongxian, Tianlongshan, Xiangtangshan, Anyang shiku diaoke*, (A Treasury of Chinese Art; Sculpture, volume 13: Gongxian, Tianlongshan, Xiangtangshan, Anyang - Cave Sculptures), Beijing, 1989, page 112, number 120 for the original position of the hands on Kashyapa, now lacking the head.[b]

## Similar examples:

Osaka Municipal Museum, *Chinese Buddhist Stone Sculpture: Veneration of the Sublime*, Osaka, 1995, page 59, number 52, for a pair of hands holding an attribute in a similar position, from the Xiangtangshan Caves; also, Mayuyama & Co. Ltd., *Mayuyama*, *Seventy Years*, volume 2, Tokyo 1976, plate 135; also, Sun Di, *Comprehensive Illustrated Catalogue of Chinese Buddhist Statues in Overseas Collection*, volume 3, Beijing, 2005, page 619; also, Katherine R. Tsiang et al., *Echoes of the Past, The Buddhist Cave Temples of Xiangtangshan*, Smart Museum of Art, Chicago, 2010, page 245, number 50.

Chen Mingda, ed., *Zhongguo meishu quanji; diaosubian 13: Gongxian, Tianlongshan, Xiangtangshan, Anyang shiku diaoke*, (A Treasury of Chinese Art; Sculpture, volume 13: Gongxian, Tianlongshan, Xiangtangshan, Anyang - Cave Sculptures), Beijing, 1989, pages 104 - 107 and pages 137 - 138 for disciples holding reliquaries in other Xiangtangshan caves.

[a] In both the 1931 and the 1939 publications, the cave is referred to as Cave 3 of the Northern Group.

[b] In this 1989 publication, the cave is referred to as Cave 4 of the Northern Group.

37
## Marble Buddha
Northern Qi or Sui period, late 6th century
Height: 41.3cm

Marble standing figure of Buddha, now missing the head, feet and hands, right arm raised and left lowered, presumably once in *abhaya* and *varada mudra*. The figure wears diaphanous monastic robes, which cover both shoulders and arms, and fall in deep U-shaped folds, with the undergarment emerging in narrow pleats at the ankles. The trailing end of the robe is draped across the partially exposed chest and fastened at the right shoulder by a tied double cord suspended from a rosette-shaped clasp, the gathered fabric arranged in fanned-out folds and the cord descending into an elaborate 'endless knot' and continuing over the forearm. The reverse of the figure is flat and undecorated except for the tip of a flaming pearl at the base. The creamy-white stone bears a soft patina.

Provenance:

Nicholas Grindley, London.

Norman A. Kurland, U. S. A.

Exhibited:

Princeton, New Jersey, 1999, Princeton University Art Museum.

Similar examples:

Palace Museum ed., *Compendium of Collections in the Palace Museum, Sculpture*, volume 7, (Buddhist Figures Unearthed at the Site of the Xiude Temple in Quyang, Hebei Province), Beijing, 2011, plates 49 - 52.

Eskenazi Limited, *Chinese Buddhist sculpture*, London, 1997, number 9 for a larger example.

The fine-textured creamy white marble of the present sculpture has allowed the sculptor to carve the details of the figure's dress with the utmost delicacy, in particular the clasp with knot at the left shoulder drawing up the edge of the robe and the endless knot in the double cord over the arm. Excavations at the site of the Xiude Temple in Quyang, Hebei province, starting in 1954, yielded over 2,200 sculptures and fragments, ranging in date from Northern Wei to Tang, all made of similar white marble and carved with similar artistry. The Palace Museum publication cited above illustrates a representative selection of sculptures from the find.

三七　理石佛像　北齐或隋代　公元六世纪晚期

高　四一·三公分

理石雕塑，立式佛宗，头部及手脚残缺，右臂抬起，左臂略低，曾施以无畏与愿印。身着袈裟，覆盖双肩及胳膊，衣褶向下，弯曲如流，僧内袍微现，皱褶于踝部。袈裟上端垂下横过胸前，系于右肩，双环结扣，悬挂花钩之上，形成扇形褶纹，向下呈精致的"方胜结"，延至小臂。佛像身后平坦素纹，仅有火焰珠的尖部于底部。乳白色的石料上有柔软的积层。

38
**Painted Earthenware Ox**
Northern Qi period, 550 - 577
Length: 38.0cm

Large grey earthenware hollow ox standing four-square on a rectangular base. The animal is modelled with characteristic hump and dewlap, its bulky body terminating in a long tail, supported by its four sturdy, hoofed legs. Its small head has well-modelled features with large eyes, prominent muzzle, pricked ears below large curved horns and is bound by a halter composed of straps set with roundels. Further pendant trappings, consisting of straps set with bosses and lions' heads with leaf-like tongues, lie across its back. Much of the original pigment remains: yellow-ochre on the body, black for the facial features and red, pink and gold leaf on the trappings.

Provenance:

James Freeman, Kyoto.

Eskenazi Limited, London.

Norman A. Kurland, U. S. A.

Exhibited:

New York, 1998, Eskenazi Limited.

Princeton, New Jersey, 1998, Princeton University Art Museum.

Published:

Eskenazi Limited, *Animals and animal designs in Chinese art*, London, 1998, number 14.

Maurizio Scarpari, *Ancient China; Chinese Civilization from the Origins to the Tang Dynasty*, Vercelli, 2000, pages 162 - 3.

Giuseppe Eskenazi in collaboration with Hajri Elias, *A Dealer's Hand, The Chinese Art Market Through the Eyes of Giuseppe Eskenazi*, London, 2012, page 254, plate 205.

Similar examples:

Ching Wan Society, *Millennium Exhibition*, Taibei, 2000, page 150, number 55.

Lin Shuzhong ed., *Zhongguo meishu quanji, diaosu bian 3, Wei Jin nanbeichao diaosu*, (The Great Treasury of Chinese Art, Sculpture 3, Six Dynasties), Beijing, 1988, page 157, number 134, for a large glazed Northern Qi ox from the tomb of Lou Rui (dated 570), Taiyuan, Shanxi province; also, James Watt et al., *China, Dawn of a Golden Age, 200 – 750 AD*, New York, 2004, number 142; also, Daiko Advertising Inc. ed., *China Crossroads of Culture*, Tokyo, 2005, page 103, number 071.

三八　彩绘陶牛　北齐　公元五五〇年—五七七年

长　三八・〇公分

灰陶胎，此牛体态硕大，空心塑造，站立于长方形底座上。形象生动，背驼和赘肉，栩栩如生，身型笨拙，长尾在后，四腿粗壮，蹄足踏地。头部偏小，精雕细琢，大眼凸吻，双耳竖起，犄角弯长。吻部佩驾具，宽带圆饰。牛沿背佩套具，含垂饰条带，镶有圆形饰。悬挂物还有鼓泡和狮面吞吐纹饰。此像大部分原色保存，米黄色身体，五官黑彩，红色粉色及金色于饰带。

188

This impressive and powerfully built figure of an ox (*niu*) embodies all the qualities of the animal which were valued in traditional Chinese culture. Oxen (or cattle) were long associated with China's agrarian tradition and, as domesticated animals, were used for ploughing, cultivating the land and pulling heavy loads. Six domestic animals, including oxen (or cattle), were reared as livestock in ancient China and were given the collective designation *liu chu* (six livestock), along with *wu gu* (five grains) in classical literature.[1] Evidence suggests that cattle were already domesticated by the Shang period – they have been found in large numbers in burial pits of that period - and their bones were certainly used in ritual divinations, as evidenced in the large quantities unearthed. In ancient texts such as the *Shi Jing* and the *Zhou Li*, references to oxen or cattle are generally in connection with the consumption of meat at banquets and rituals, although there is the occasional mention of cattle as 'draught animals for carrying provisions and pulling carts in military operations.'[2] Although less glamorous than horses, oxen were, nevertheless, admired for their strength, endurance and patience; the ox is one of the animals of the Chinese zodiac and also features in Chinese mythology, such as in the story of the ox-herd and the weaver girl, lovers separated by the Milky Way except for one night a year.

While the ox was primarily a draught animal, during the Six Dynasties period it appears that the ox-drawn canopied cart (*ziping*) replaced the horse-drawn chariot as a popular form of transport for the rich and aristocratic members of society. It has been suggested that this was part of a widespread rejection of the ostentatious display of wealth and the embracing of a 'simple life'; or it may have had a more practical basis – such as the shortage of horses due to constant warfare. The ox-drawn cart may have also featured in ritual mourning rites: 'officials started to ride in ox-drawn carts in certain stages of mourning rites', as recorded in the *Jinshu* (History of the Jin).[3] In addition to the earthenware models of oxen and ox-drawn carts often found in Six Dynasties tombs, there are also depictions of them on the sides of stone sarcophagi, such as that found in the Northern Wei tomb at Zhijiabao, Datong, Shanxi[4] and on wall murals, such as the ones in the Northern Qi tomb of Xu Xianxiu (502 - 571), Taiyuan, Shanxi.[5] The present example bears many similarities to the ox on the tomb murals of Xu Xianxiu, including the halter around the head and the elaborate trappings hanging across the back, suggesting that it was intended to represent an ox with a ceremonial function.

[1] H. T. Huang, *Science and Civilisation in China*, volume 6, Cambridge, 2000, page 55.

[2] H. T. Huang, op. cit., page 57.

[3] Susan L. Beningson, 'Negotiating the Afterlife in Tombs of the Northern and Southern Dynasties', in Willow Weilan Hai, Annette L. Juliano et al., *Art in a Time of Chaos, Masterworks from Six Dynasties China 3rd - 6th Centuries*, New York, 2016, pages 130 - 131.

[4] Susan L. Beningson, op. cit., page 129, figure 3.

[5] Shi Jinming, 'The Northern Dynasties and Major Archaeological Discoveries', in Willow Weilan Hai, Annette L. Juliano et al., *Art in a Time of Chaos, Masterworks from Six Dynasties China 3rd - 6th Centuries*, New York, 2016, pages 74 - 75.

## Previous Exhibitions

| | |
|---|---|
| March 1972 | Inaugural exhibition Early Chinese ceramics and works of art. |
| June 1972 | Georges Rouault, an exhibition arranged by Richard Nathanson. |
| June 1973 | Ancient Chinese bronze vessels, gilt bronzes and early ceramics. |
| November 1973 | Chinese ceramics from the Cottle collection. |
| December 1973 | Japanese netsuke formerly in the collection of Dr Robert L Greene. |
| June 1974 | Early Chinese ceramics and works of art. |
| November 1974 | Japanese inrō from the collection of E A Wrangham. |
| May 1975 | Japanese netsuke and inrō from private collections. |
| June 1975 | Ancient Chinese bronzes from the Stoclet and Wessén collections. |
| June 1976 | Chinese jades from a private collection. |
| June 1976 | Michael Birch netsuke and sculpture. |
| June 1976 | Japanese netsuke and inrō from private collections. |
| June 1977 | Ancient Chinese bronze vessels, gilt bronzes and sculptures; two private collections, one formerly part of the Minkenhof collection. |
| June 1978 | Ancient Chinese sculpture. |
| June 1978 | Michael Webb netsuke. |
| June 1978 | Eighteenth to twentieth century netsuke. |
| June 1979 | Japanese netsuke from private collections. |
| June 1980 | Japanese netsuke from private collections and Michael Webb netsuke. |
| July 1980 | Ancient Chinese bronzes and gilt bronzes from the Wessén and other collections. |
| December 1980 | Chinese works of art from the collection of J M A J Dawson. |
| October 1981 | Japanese netsuke and inrō from the collection of Professor and Mrs John Hull Grundy and other private collections. |
| December 1981 | Ancient Chinese sculpture. |
| October 1982 | Japanese inrō from private collections. |
| November 1983 | Michael Webb, an English carver of netsuke. |
| October 1984 | Japanese netsuke, ojime, inrō and lacquer-ware. |
| June 1985 | Ancient Chinese bronze vessels, gilt bronzes, inlaid bronzes, silver, jades, ceramics – Twenty five years. |
| December 1986 | Japanese netsuke, ojime, inrō and lacquer-ware. |
| June 1987 | Tang. |
| June 1989 | Chinese and Korean art from the collections of Dr Franco Vannotti, Hans Popper and others. |
| November 1989 | Japanese lacquer-ware from the Verbrugge collection. |
| December 1989 | Chinese art from the Reach family collection. |
| May 1990 | Japanese netsuke from the Lazarnick collection. |
| June 1990 | Ancient Chinese sculpture from the Alsdorf collection and others. |
| November 1990 | The Charles A Greenfield collection of Japanese lacquer. |
| June 1991 | Inlaid bronze and related material from pre-Tang China. |
| November 1992 | Japanese lacquer-ware – recent acquisitions. |
| December 1992 | Chinese lacquer from the Jean-Pierre Dubosc collection and others. |
| June 1993 | Early Chinese art from tombs and temples. |
| June 1993 | Japanese netsuke from the Carré collection. |
| June 1994 | Yuan and early Ming blue and white porcelain. |
| June 1995 | Early Chinese art: 8th century BC – 9th century AD. |
| October 1995 | Adornment for Eternity, loan exhibition from the Denver Art Museum. |
| June 1996 | Sculpture and ornament in early Chinese art. |
| November 1996 | Japanese inrō and lacquer-ware from a private Swedish collection. |
| March 1997 | Ceramic sculpture from Han and Tang China. |
| June 1997 | Chinese Buddhist sculpture. |
| June 1997 | Japanese netsuke, ojime and inrō from the Dawson collection. |
| November 1997 | Japanese netsuke – recent acquisitions. |
| March 1998 | Animals and animal designs in Chinese art. |

| | |
|---|---|
| June 1998 | Japanese netsuke, ojime and inrō from a private European collection. |
| November 1998 | Chinese works of art and furniture. |
| March 1999 | Ancient Chinese bronzes and ceramics. |
| November 1999 | Ancient Chinese bronzes from an English private collection. |
| March 2000 | Masterpieces from ancient China. |
| November 2000 | Chinese furniture of the 17th and 18th centuries. |
| March 2001 | Tang ceramic sculpture. |
| November 2001 | Chinese ceramic vessels 500 – 1000 AD. |
| March 2002 | Chinese Buddhist sculpture from Northern Wei to Ming. |
| November 2002 | Two rare Chinese porcelain fish jars of the 14th and 16th centuries. |
| March 2003 | Chinese works of art from the Stoclet collection. |
| November 2003 | Song: Chinese ceramics, 10th to 13th century. |
| March 2004 | Chinese Buddhist figures. |
| November 2004 | A selection of Ming and Qing porcelain. |
| March 2005 | Ancient Chinese bronzes and sculpture. |
| November 2005 | Song ceramics from the Hans Popper collection. |
| March 2006 | A selection of early Chinese bronzes. |
| June 2006 | Recent paintings by Arnold Chang. |
| November 2006 | Chinese porcelain from the 15th to the 18th century. |
| March 2007 | Song: Chinese ceramics, 10th to 13th century (part 3). |
| November 2007 | Mountain landscapes by Li Huayi. |
| March 2008 | Chinese sculpture and works of art. |
| October 2008 | Chinese ceramics and stone sculpture. |
| October 2009 | Seven classical Chinese paintings. |
| March 2010 | Trees, rocks, mist and mountains by Li Huayi. |
| November 2010 | Fiftieth anniversary exhibition: twelve Chinese masterworks. |
| March 2011 | Early Chinese metalwork in gold and silver; works of art of the Ming and Qing dynasties. |
| November 2011 | Chinese huanghuali furniture from a private collection. |
| November 2011 | The twelve animals of the zodiac by Li Huayi. |
| November 2012 | Qing porcelain from a private collection. |
| October 2013 | Junyao. |
| October 2013 | Bo Ju Gui: an important Chinese archaic bronze. |
| October 2014 | Waterfalls, rocks and bamboo by Li Huayi. |
| October 2014 | Chinese sculpture c. 500 - 1500. |
| May 2015 | Principal wares of the Song period from a private collection. |
| October 2015 | Transfigured echoes: recent paintings by Liu Dan. |
| October 2016 | Recent paintings by Zeng Xiaojun. |
| November 2016 | Early Chinese art from private collections. |